Craters of Fire

By the same author:

CAVES OF ADVENTURE

CRATERS OF FIRE

HAROUN TAZIEFF

TRANSLATED FROM THE FRENCH BY
EITHNE WILKINS

HARPER & BROTHERS
PUBLISHERS, NEW YORK

Library of Congress catalog card number: 53-11860

CONTENTS

Three sections of photographs
follow pages 64, 128, and 192

And the Queen the sorceress who fans the live embers in her earthen pot will never tell us what she knows and what we do not know.

RIMBAUD, *Les Illuminations*

CRATERS OF FIRE

CHAPTER I

NOT A VERY SENSIBLE PLACE
FOR A STROLL

I tossed off an immense gulp of poison.

Rimbaud, *Une saison en Enfer*

STANDING on the summit of the growling cone, even
before I got my breath back after the stiff climb, I peered
down into the crater.

I was astonished. Two days previously the red lava had
been boiling up to the level of the gigantic lip; now the
funnel seemed to be empty. All that incandescent magma
had disappeared, drawn back into the depths by the reflux
of some mysterious ebb and flow, a sort of breathing. But
there, about fifty feet below where I was standing, was the
glow and the almost animate fury of the great throat which
volcanologists call the conduit or chimney. It was quite a
while before I could tear my eyes away from that lurid,
fiery centre, that weird palpitation of the abyss. At
intervals of about a minute, heralded each time by a

dry clacking, bursts of projectiles were flung up, running away up into the air, speading out fan-wise, all aglare, and then falling back, whistling, on the outer sides of the cone. I was rather tense, ready to leap aside at any moment, as I watched these showers, with their menacing trajectories.

Each outburst of rage was followed by a short lull. Then heavy rolls of brown and bluish fumes came puffing out, while a muffled grumbling, rather like that of some monstrous watch-dog, set the whole bulk of the volcano quivering. There was not much chance for one's nerves to relax, so swiftly did each follow on the other—the sudden tremor, the burst, the momentary intensification of the incandescence, and the outbreak of a fresh salvo. The bombs went roaring up, the cone of fire opening out overhead, while I hung in suspense. Then came the hissing and sizzling, increasing in speed and intensity, each 'whoosh' ending up in a muffled thud as the bomb fell. On their black bed of scoriae, the clots of molten magma lay with the fire slowly dying out of them, one after the other growing dark and cold.

Some minutes of observation were all I needed. I noted that today, apart from three narrow zones to the west, north, and north-east, the edges of the crater had scarcely been damaged at all by the barrage from underground. The southern point where I stood was a mound rising some twelve or fifteen feet above the general level of the rim, that narrow, crumbling lip of scoriae nearer to the fire, where I had never risked setting foot. I looked at this rather alarming ledge all round the crater, and gradually felt an increasing desire to do something about it . . . It became irresistible. After all, as the level of the column of lava had dropped to such an exceptional degree, was this not the moment to try what I was so tempted to do and go right round the crater?

Still, I hesitated. This great maw, these jaws sending out heat that was like the heavy breathing of some living creature, thoroughly frightened me. Leaning forward over that hideous glow, I was no longer a geologist in search of information, but a terrified savage.

'If I lose my grip,' I said aloud, 'I shall simply run for it.'

The sound of my own voice restored me to normal awareness of myself. I got back my critical sense and began to think about what I could reasonably risk trying. 'De l'audace, encore de l'audace. . . .' That was all very well, of course, but one must also be careful. Past experience whispered a warning not to rush into anything blindly. Getting the upper hand of both anxiety and impatience, I spent several minutes considering, with the greatest of care, the monster's manner of behaving. Solitude has got me into the habit of talking to myself, and so it was more or less aloud that I gave myself permission to go ahead.

'Right, then. It can be done.'

I turned up my collar and buttoned my canvas jacket tight at the throat—I didn't want a sly cinder down the back of my neck! Then I tucked what was left of my hair under an old felt hat that did service for a helmet. And now for it!

Very cautiously indeed, I approach the few yards of pretty steep slope separating the peak from the rim I am going to explore. I cross, in a gingerly manner, a first incandescent crevasse. It is intense orange in colour and quivering with heat, as though opening straight into a mass of glowing embers. The fraction of a second it takes me to cross it is just long enough for it to scorch the thick cord of my breeches. I get a strong whiff of burnt wool.

A promising start, I must say!

Here comes a second break in the ground. Damn it, a wide one, too! I can't just stride across this one: I'll have to jump it. The incline makes me thoughtful. Standing there, I consider the unstable slope of scoriae that will have to serve me for a landing-ground. If I don't manage to pull up . . . if I go rolling along down this funnel with the flames lurking at the bottom of it . . . My little expedition all at once strikes me as thoroughly rash, and I stay where I am, hesitating. But the heat under my feet is becoming unbearable. I can't endure it except by shifting around. It only needs ten seconds of standing still on this enemy territory, with the burning gases slowly and steadily seeping through it, and the soles of my feet are already baking hot. From second to second the alternative becomes increasingly urgent: I must jump for it or retreat.

Here I am! I have landed some way down the fissure. The ashes slide underfoot, but I stop without too much trouble. As so often happens, the anxiety caused by the obstacle made me over-estimate its importance.

Step by step, I set out on my way along the wide wall of slag-like debris that forms a sort of fortification all round the precipice. The explosions are still going on at regular intervals of between sixty and eighty seconds. So far no projectile has come down on this side, and this cheers me up considerably. With marked satisfaction I note that it is pretty rare for two bombs of the same salvo to fall less than three yards apart: the average distance between them seems to be one of several paces. This is encouraging. One of the great advantages of this sort of bombardment, compared with one by artillery, lies in the relative slowness with which the projectiles fall, the eye being able to follow them quite easily. Furthermore, these shells don't burst. But what an uproar, what an enormous, prolonged bellowing accompanies their being hurled out of the bowels of the earth!

I make use of a brief respite in order to get quickly across the ticklish north-eastern sector. Then I stop for a few seconds, just long enough to see yet another burst gush up and come showering down a little ahead of me, after which I start out for the conquest of the northern sector. Here the crest narrows down so much that it becomes a mere ridge, where walking is so difficult and balancing so precarious that I find myself forced to go on along the outer slope, very slightly lower down. Little by little, as I advance through all this tumult, a feeling of enthusiasm is overtaking me. The immediate imperative necessity for action has driven panic far into the background. And under the hot, dry skin of my face, taut on forehead and cheekbones, I can feel my compressed lips parting, of their own accord, in a smile of sheer delight. But look out!

A sudden intensification of the light warns me that I am approaching a point right in the prolongation of the fiery chimney. In fact, the chimney is not vertical, but slightly inclined in a north-westerly direction, and from here one can look straight down into it. These tellurian entrails, brilliantly yellow, seem to be surging with heat. The sight is so utterly amazing that I stand there, transfixed.

Suddenly, before I can make any move, the dazzling yellow changes to white, and in the same instant I feel a muffled tremor all through my body and there is a

thunderous uproar in my ears. The burst of incandescent
blocks is already in full swing. My throat tightens as,
motionless, I follow with my gaze the clusters of red lumps
rising in slow, perfect curves. There is an instant of un-
certainty. And then down comes the hail of fire.

This time the warning was too short: I am right in
the middle of it all. With my shoulders hunched up, head
drawn back, chin in air, buttocks as much tucked in as
possible, I peer up into the vault of sinister whining and
whizzing there above me. All around bombs are crashing
down, still pasty and soft, making a succession of muffled
plops. One dark mass seems to have singled me out and is
making straight for my face. Instinctively I take a leap to
one side, and *feel* the great lump flatten itself out a few
inches from my left foot. I should like to have a look,
but this is not the moment! Here comes another projectile.
I take another leap to dodge it. It lands close beside me.
Then suddenly the humming in the air begins to thin out.
There are a few more whizzing sounds, and then the
downpour is over.

Have you ever tried to imagine a snail's state of mind
as it creeps out of its shell again, the danger past? That
was the way my head, which had been drawn back between
hunched-up shoulders, gradually began to rise up again
on my neck, and my arched back began to straighten,
my arms to loosen, my hands to unclench. Right, then—
it's better not to hang about in this sector! So I set out
again. By this time I have got round three-quarters of the
crater, and am in the gap between the northern and western
zones, which are those that get the worst pounding. From
here I can get back on to the ridge proper.

I am now almost directly over the roaring chasm, and
my gaze goes straight down into it like a stone dropping
into the pit. After all, it's nothing but a tunnel. That's
all. It's a vertical tunnel, ten or fifteen yards across, its
walls heated to such a degree that they stretch and 'rise'
like dough, and up from its depths every now and then
enormous drops of liquid fire spurt forth, a great splashing

sweat that falls and vanishes, golden flash upon flash, back into the dazzling gulf. Even the brownish vapours emanating from the pit cannot quite veil its splendour. It is nothing but a tunnel running down into viscous copper-coloured draperies; yet it opens into the very substance of another world. The sight is so extraordinary that I forget the insecurity of my position and the hellish burning under the soles of my feet. Quite mechanically, I go on lifting first the left foot, then the right. It is as though my mind were held fast in a trap by the sight of this burning well from which a terrifying snore continually rises, interrupted by sharp explosions and the rolling of thunder.

Suddenly I hurl myself backwards. The flight of projectiles has whizzed past my face. Hunched up again, instinctively trying to make as small a target of myself as I can, I once more go through the horrors that I am beginning to know. I am in the thick of this hair's-breadth game of anticipation and dodging.

And now it's all over; I take a last glance into the marvellous and terrible abyss, and am just getting ready to start off on the last stage of this burning circumnavigation, all two hundred yards of it, when I get a sudden sharp blow in the back. A delayed-action bomb! With all the breath knocked out of me, I stand rigid.

A moment passes. I wonder why I am not dead. But nothing seems to have happened to me—no pain, no change of any sort. Slowly I risk turning my head, and at my feet I see a sort of huge red loaf with the glow dying out of it.

I stretch my arms and wriggle my back. Nothing hurts. Everything seems to be in its proper place. Later on, examining my jacket, I discovered a brownish scorch-mark with slightly charred edges, about the size of my hand, and I drew from it a conclusion of immense value to me in future explorations: so long as one is not straight in the line of fire, volcanic bombs, which fall in a still pasty state, but already covered with a kind of very thin elastic skin, graze one without having time to cause a deep burn.

I set off at a run, as lightly as my 165 pounds allow, for I must be as quick as I can in crossing this part of the crater-edge, which is one of the most heavily bombarded. But I am assailed by an unexpected blast of suffocating fumes. My eyes close, full of smarting tears. I am caught in a cloud of gas forced down by the wind. I fight for breath. It feels as if I were swallowing lumps of dry, corrosive cotton-wool. My head swims, but I urge myself at all costs to get the upper hand. The main thing is not to breathe this poisoned air. Groping, I fumble in a pocket. Damn, not this one. How about this other one, then? No. At last I get a handkerchief out and, still with my eyes shut, cover my mouth with it. Then, stumbling along, I try to get through the loathsome cloud. I no longer even bother to pay any attention to the series of bursts from the volcano, being too anxious to get out of this hell before I lose grip entirely. I am getting pretty exhausted, staggering . . . The air filtered through the handkerchief just about keeps me going, but it is still too poisonous, and there is too little of it for the effort involved in making this agonising journey across rough and dangerous terrain. The gases are too concentrated, and the great maw that is belching them forth is too near.

A few steps ahead of me I catch a glimpse of the steep wall of the peak, or promontory, from the other side of which I started about a century ago, it seems to me now. The noxious mists are licking round the peak, which is almost vertical and twice the height of a man. It's so near! But I realise at once that I shall never have the strength to clamber up it.

In less than a second, the few possible solutions to this life-and-death problem race through my mind. Shall I turn my back to the crater and rush away down the outer slope, which is bombarded by the thickest barrages? No. About face and back along the ledge? Whatever I do, I must turn back. And then make my escape. By sliding

down the northern slope? That is also under too heavy
bombardment. And the worst of it would be that in
making a descent of that sort there would be no time to
keep a watch for blocks of lava coming down on one.

Only one possibility is left: to make my way back all
along the circular ridge, more than a hundred yards of it,
till I reach the eastern rim, where neither gas nor projectiles are so concentrated as to be necessarily fatal.

I swing round. I stumble and collapse on all fours,
uncovering my mouth for an instant. The gulp of gas
that I swallow hurts my lungs, and leaves me gasping.
Red-hot scoriae are embedded in the palms of my hands.
I shall never get out of this!

The first fifteen or twenty steps of this journey back
through the acrid fumes of sulphur and chlorine are a slow
nightmare; no step means any progress and no breath
brings any oxygen into the lungs. The threat of bombs
no longer counts. Only these gases exist now. Air! Air!

I came to myself again on the eastern rim, gasping down
the clean air borne by the wind, washing out my lungs
with deep fresh gulps of it, as though I could never get
enough. How wide and comfortable this ledge is! What a
paradise compared with the suffocating, torrid hell from
which I have at last escaped! And yet this is where I was
so anxious and so tense less than a quarter of an hour
ago.

Several draughts of the prevailing breeze have relieved
my ágony. All at once, life is again worth living! I no
longer feel that desire to escape from here as swiftly as
possible. On the contrary, I feel a new upsurge of explorer's
curiosity. Once more my gaze turns towards the mouth,
out of which sporadic bursts of grape-shot are still spurting
forth. Now and then there are bigger explosions and I
have to keep a look-out for what may come down on my
head, which momentarily interrupts the dance I keep up
from one foot to the other, that *tresca* of which Dante
speaks—the dance of the damned, harried by fire. True,
I have come to the conclusion that the impact of these

bombs is not necessarily fatal, but I am in no hurry to verify the observation.

The inner walls of the crater do not all incline at the same angle. To the north, west and south, they are practically vertical, not to say overhanging, but here on the east the slope drops away at an angle of no more than fifty degrees. So long as one moved along in a gingerly way, this might be an incline one could negotiate. It would mean going down into the very heart of the volcano. For an instant I am astounded by my own foolhardiness. Still, it's really too tempting . . .

Cautiously, I take a step forward . . . then another . . . and another . . . seems all right . . . it *is* all right. I begin the climb down, digging my heels as deep as I can into the red-hot scoriae. Gradually below me, the oval of the enormous maw comes nearer, growing bigger, and the terrifying uproar becomes more deafening. My eyes, open as wide as they will go, are drunken with its monstrous glory. Here are those ponderous draperies of molten gold and copper, so near—so near that I feel as if I, human being that I am, had entered right into their fabulous world. The air is stifling hot. I am right in the fiery furnace.

I linger before this fascinating spectacle. But then, by sheer effort, I tear myself away. It's time to get back to being 'scientific' and measure the temperatures, of the ground, and of the atmosphere. I plunge the long spike of the thermometer into the shifting scoriae, and the steel of it glitters among these brownish and grey screes with their dull shimmer. At a depth of six inches the temperature is two hundred and twenty degrees centigrade. It's amusing to think that when I used to dream it was always about polar exploration!

Suddenly, the monster vomits out another burst; so close that the noise deafens me. I bury my face in my arms. Fortunately almost every one of the projectiles comes down outside the crater. And now all at once I realise that it is I who am here—*alive* in this crater, surrounded by scorching walls, face to face with the very mouth of the fire.

Why have I got myself into this trap, alone and without the slightest chance of help? Nobody in the world has any suspicion of the strange adventure on which I have embarked, and nobody, for that matter, could now do the slightest thing about it. Better not think about it . . .

Without a break the grim, steady growling continues to rise from the depths of that throat, only out-roared at intervals by the bellowing and belching of lava. It's too much; I can feel myself giving up. I turn my back on it, and try, on all fours, to scramble up the slope, which has now become incredibly steep and crumbles and gives way under my weight, which is dragging me down, down . . . 'Steady, now,' I say to myself. 'Keep calm for a moment. Let's work it out. Let's work it out properly. Or else, my boy, this is the end of *you*.'

Little by little, by immense exertions, I regain control of my movements, as well as the mental steadiness I need. I persuade myself to climb *calmly* up this short slope, which keeps crumbling away under my feet. When I reach the top, I stand upright for just a moment. Then, crossing the two glowing fissures that still intersect my course, I reach the part of the rim from where there is a way down to the world of ordinary peaceful things.

CHAPTER II

THE MAKING OF A VOLCANOLOGIST

'WHAT was he doing in that crater, anyhow?' the reader will wonder. Actually, this is what I was just going to ask myself. What was I doing there?

It will perhaps be a little difficult to grasp the fact that four or five weeks before that first descent into the erupting crater of Kituro, I was no more familiar with a volcano in Central Africa, or with lava and eruptions, than we earth-dwellers are with the surface of the moon. My knowledge of volcanoes, which was pretty rudimentary, came entirely from books, and was quite enough to keep me happy. I practically never thought about the subject.

It was scarcely two months since I had left Katanga, where I had spent two years in search of, and extracting, tin ore. What had brought me to Kivu, a mountainous region in the north-east of the Belgian Congo, was the presence there of a geologist of outstanding reputation, and my wish to work under his direction. As bad luck would have it, this remarkable man died shortly before I arrived, and his team, not quite knowing what to do with this new recruit, sent me off on the job of making a geological map somewhere between Tanganyika and Lake Kivu. This country, which enjoys a fine reputation, to me seemed rather boring. I quickly came to sigh for the luxuriantly stifling heat of 'down-country' in the broiling, sun-soaked, typically tropical Congo. Here the relative

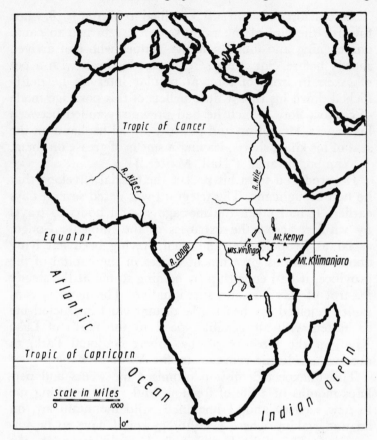

coolness and the often cloudy sky perhaps reminded me a little too much of my own melancholy north, but without conveying those nostalgic feelings that depend on memory. For one reason or another, I remained insensitive to the charm of those high hills covered with a thin grassy savannah.

All in all, it was sheer professional conscientiousness that kept me at a job the result of which would all too probably moulder among dusty records in a library. Stoically I counted the weeks that lay between me and my return to Europe.

At least forty of them still remained to March 1948, when towards the end of the rainy season I returned to camp one evening and found a native runner who had arrived shortly before. Squatting serenely on his heels with a pot of *bukari* in front of him, at regular intervals he deftly flicked down his throat little pellets of this porridge made of cassava flour, which he had previously rolled between his fingers. He got up and placidly wiped his hand on the seat of his khaki shorts, leaving a smear of grease on them.

'Yambo, Bwana.' ('Hail, Master.')

He produced from his pocket the official envelope that he had brought me. The telegram was dated several days earlier. It had taken the message several hours to travel by wireless across the expanses of the immense Congo, as far as Léopoldville, and then, having been left lying about in various government offices in the capital of the province, it had ended up by coming to me at the steady jog-trot of this bureaucratised native. The news it contained rejoiced my heart. My distant chief instructed me to hasten with all possible speed to the north of Lake Kivu, in the territory of the Albert National Park, to observe a volcanic eruption in the Virunga Range.

This unexpected mission promised me weeks and perhaps months of a life of freedom and variety, taking me to new scenery and, I imagined, wild mountain air, on an undertaking where everything would have to be improvised. The difficulties, which I could guess at, the prospect of rough living spiced, no doubt, with still more or less undefined dangers—all these were additional attractions.

Already, while I was doing honour to the grilled banana served by my 'boy' Paya, I saw looming up before me the mass of the eight volcanoes that form the Virunga Range: eight giants reared up on a vast plateau of lava at which the jungle nibbled. I knew that six of them, with altitudes of between 10,800 and 14,800 feet, were considered definitely extinct, but that two others, at the western end of the range, were still active. Which of the two had suddenly burst into renewed virulence? Was it Nyamlagira, 9,840 feet in height, which had been dormant since 1940, after an eruption lasting two years? Or was it Niragongo, that mighty truncated cone towering to a height of almost 11,500 feet over the blue meanderings of Lake Kivu? A plume of steam formed a permanent crown to it. In the course of one of my trips I had seen this plume aglow in

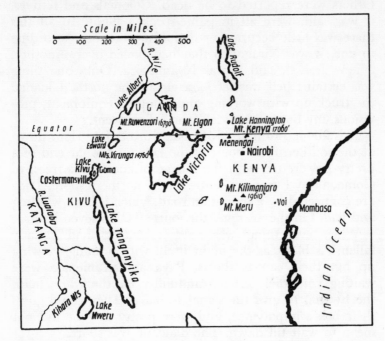

the night, lit up by the flames of lava in the immense crater. That night again, although I was so far away, it went on glowing for a long time in my half-sleep . . .

From the geological laboratory at Bukavu[1] I carried off everything I could lay hands on in the way of volcanological instruments. It wasn't much. To make up for that, however, there was no shortage of rumours about the cataclysm. The whole of the little town was aquiver with news

---

[1] The native name for Costermansville, also known, more briefly, as Coste, the capital of the vast province of Kivu.

as confusing as it was terrifying. 'The town of Goma is
fated, the lava has reached the first houses . . . No, it's
Ruchuru that's threatened by the streams of lava . . .'
A motorist, getting out of his car and taking off his helmet
to wipe his forehead, shouted that all the roads were cut.
One was told the names of planters whose quinquina or
pyrethrum farms had been covered by the rain of ashes.
Others were reported to be dead. Colonials and natives,
it was said, were all in panic-stricken flight. In all this
there was little accurate or useful information. According
to one, it was Niragongo that had boiled over. Another,
a new arrival, said it was Nyamlagira. Only one thing
was certain: hell was let loose up in the north. I loaded
the truck up with working and camping equipment, provisions, my boys and myself, and off we went.

It is about 140 miles from Bukavu, nestling right down
at the southernmost point of the lake, at the far end of a
pretty bay fretted with the foliage of eucalyptus trees, to
Goma, a tiny European centre on the northern shore. They
are connected by a mountain road, which is both winding
and bad. On the average, the journey takes seven hours.

When everything was ready, darkness had already
fallen. As black as the night itself, with nothing showing
up but their canvas shorts, Paya and Kaniepala were
waiting with their usual tranquillity for the white man,
the Bwana, to give the signal to leave. They could guess
their boss's impatience, and were pretty sure he did not
mean to wait till dawn. The dialogue was short.

'Alafu, Paya, tunakwenda?' ('Well, Paya, shall we get
moving?')

'Kabisa, Bwana!' ('And how, Master!')

The doors of the truck slammed. Kaniepala jumped up
behind and, rolling himself up in his blanket, went straight
off to sleep among the boxes. I lit the headlamps. For
once the engine started without giving any trouble, as
though it too had been infected with our haste, and then
we were off.

As I drove, I began to consider my new job.

A geologist who goes in for volcanoes, I said to myself, must be called a *volcanologist* . . . The idea of the mission pleased me more and more, but I began to feel some uneasiness when I thought of how little knowledge I had of the subject. Sitting on a bench in a lecture-room, I had paid precious little attention to these pustules on the body of the earth. Our teachers, extremely learned when it was a matter of phenomena dating from several millions of years ago or of what must be going on several thousands of leagues down under the earth, were rather disdainful about these all-too-contemporary manifestations on the surface. And so, realising my ignorance, I had spent the previous afternoon rummaging through the official library at Coste, in an effort to find a handbook of volcanology. But in vain. Despite its proximity to volcanoes, the library seemed equally determined to ignore the subject. In despair of finding what I wanted, I had had to fall back on the 'Volcanoes' chapter in a general work on geology; and I must say it was excellent as far as it went. Altogether I was feeling slightly at a loss. Still, I thought to myself, while the truck was contending with the most wanton corkscrew bends in the road, had it not always been thus in any colony? There everyone learns for himself, by sheer trial and error, how to do what, in theory, he knows nothing about, and nobody does the thing he has been trained for. The mechanic builds houses, the prospector nurses the sick, the retired sea-faring man plants coffee . . . and in the long run everyone manages somehow. A geologist who has done some surface-mining should be able to get along quite well in volcanology!

As far as actual volcanoes went, all I had ever really seen was the peak at Teneriffe, that superb bulk of dark indigo outlined against the liquid gold of the sunset sky. Superb, of course, but not much to go on in the way of scientific information . . . The ship had kept steadily on her course, without calling there. For the rest, there had been certain exceptionally clear nights when from Bukavu I had been able to look across sixty miles of lake-water to

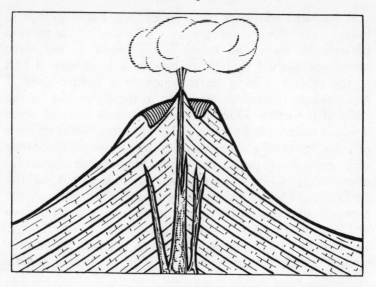

where Niragongo sent up the lurid glow that had just been haunting my vigil. Some time previously I had even crossed that Virunga Range towards which we were at this moment driving, but the weather had been too thick for us to see much of our surroundings.

Naturally enough, like everyone else I knew that there were *active* volcanoes, which may be either dormant or in eruption, and those that are *extinct*. I also knew that they are all situated on important cracks in the crust of the earth, cracks that are produced in places where the crust is weak, generally on the edge of deep oceanic faults. And furthermore I knew that certain volcanoes are violently explosive, whereas others behave in a manner that is essentially effusive; some send out viscous lava, others fluid lava.

And finally, I knew that although the general form of the volcano is the conic mountain with a crater opening at the summit, there are also others: the 'shield' volcano, the volcano with a 'plug dome', the 'strato-volcano', which has for a crater a vast 'sink-hole', a sort of caved-in

cylindrical tank pierced by one or more shafts, also cylindrical, and again the kind called *caldera* (the Spanish for 'cauldron')—immense craters with a more or less horizontal floor covered with smaller cones, as well as pits and fractures.

But what did I know of the *why* behind volcanic phenomena, the force driving to the surface the magma from the depths of the earth? Of all the aspects of my ignorance, the most serious, in my own eyes, was ignorance of the volcanologist's *job*. There was nothing definite in my mind but my haste to get there, my good will, and a curiosity ready for anything. Doubtless this was a great deal, but it was, perhaps, scarcely enough. I tried, without much success, to imagine what was waiting for me and to work out the plan of attack. These reflections filled hour after hour of my journey, jolting along through the darkness.

CHAPTER III

VOLCANOES AND ERUPTIONS

VOLCANOES mark out certain regions where the crust of the earth is weaker, over areas of hundreds, sometimes even thousands, of miles. The most famous of these belts is the Belt of Fire in the Pacific. But there are plenty of others: in the ocean, in Central Africa, along the edge of certain parts of the Atlantic and of the Indian Ocean, and in the deep and geologically ancient fault that is the Mediterranean. At the present time there are estimated to be more than six hundred active volcanoes, running out in long chains in various parts of the earth. To this must be added a number of 'extinct' volcanoes—some that are reputed to be so, at least, since it is sometimes rash to pronounce really 'dead' a volcano situated in an active region. When the ancestor of the present Vesuvius exploded in 79 A.D., burying Herculaneum and Pompeii, it was believed to have become harmless. The charred remains that have been got out of the bed of ashes, even several centuries later, and which are to be seen in the museum at Pompeii, bear witness to the terrible shocks to which man's confidence is subject.

Are the inhabitants of Auvergne or Scotland exposed to such appalling surprises? No, we may be fairly sure of that. At least it seems reasonable to think that the very advanced state of erosion of the volcanic cones in these regions means that thousands of years have passed away since the last eruption.[1]

Volcanoes are referred to as 'dormant' or 'inactive' when the only activity is the exhalation of volcanic vapours, or fumeroles, between two less peaceful periods. The vapours are exhaled from fissures on the sides as well as within the crater itself. They consist of various gases, chiefly sulphur dioxide, hydrochloric acid, sulphuretted hydrogen, ammonia, carbon dioxide, alkaline chlorides, sulphur, azote, and above all water-vapour. These volcanic vapours are of varying degrees of heat and their composition also differs according to time and situation, in one place seeping out languidly and at another bursting forth with great violence.

Nyamlagira in Kivu Province has been dormant for ten years. Vesuvius has been quiet since its great eruption in 1944. Mount Hekla, in Iceland, has been quiet since the eruption of 1947, Mount Pelée in Martinique since 1929, Vulcano, in the Islands of Lipari, since 1890. The greater part of the vents making up the Pacific Belt of Fire remains dormant between violent eruptions. Study of, above all, the temperature, the composition and the vapours of these great dozing monsters makes it possible to forecast an eruption and to save many lives by evacuating the threatened populations in time. The Dutch in the East Indies, the Japanese in their archipelago, and the Russians in Kamchatka, have in this way avoided the loss of hundreds of thousands of human lives.

Some volcanoes, on the other hand, are never, or at least very rarely, dormant between paroxysms. During these periods when the incandescent lava does not pour out, it still remains very close to the surface. Sometimes this fermentation begins after a fairly short lull and is the prelude to an eruption: Vesuvius, for example. The crater of Stromboli is always full of molten lava; thrust upwards

[1] There are, likewise, extinct volcanoes in other parts of the globe—the Deccan, the Sahara, Greenland, the Eiffel district of the Rhineland—that did provide conditions favourable to the rising of magma from the depths—millions of years ago.

by magmatic gases, it is ceaselessly flung into the air, and there are hardly more than a few minutes between explosions. Kilauea, in Hawaii, Sawaii in the Samoan archipelago, Kliouchev in Kamchatka, Erebus on the fringe of the Antarctic continent, and also Niragongo in the Virunga Range in the Congo, all have this strange peculiarity of harbouring a lake of living lava in the depths of their vast cylindrical crater. This type of volcano is known as 'Hawaian'. The lake of fire goes on seething for years on end, its level rising and falling, and violent bubblings, known as 'fountains', appear at points on the surface where the gases break through out of the depths; these 'fountains' may reach a height of a hundred feet or more. When the level of the lake rises, what happens sooner or later is that the lava fills the crater to the rim and overflows. Or again, the walls of the mighty cone may break under the pressure of these terrific underground forces and the escaping lava then goes pouring in torrents down the outer slopes: that is what is called a *mass* eruption.

For just as there are various different types of volcanoes, so too there are various kinds of eruption.

The Hawaian volcanoes and those of Iceland,[1] as well as the majority of those found at the heart of the great oceans, emit extremely fluid lava flows which sometimes cover immense areas.

Laki, or Skaptar Jökull, stands not far from the southern coast of Iceland, a country not only of ice, as its name proclaims, but also of fire. On 11 June 1783, after several seismic tremors and the emission of profuse vapours, the volcano began to pour out torrents of liquid lava, through a series of vents in a line along a fissure twelve miles in length. These torrents very soon joined, forming broad incandescent rivers. One of these, plunging down into the valley where the little river Skalta flowed, turned it to steam and sent a fiery flood into the gorges, six hundred

---

[1] Twenty-five historically active volcanoes and a hundred and seven known, with thousands of vents.

feet deep, which the waters had taken thousands of years to hollow out. Then the lava overflowed in one place after another, spreading in all directions. This appalling stream flowed on into a lake, the waters of which were partly turned into steam, while the rest rushed down, in an avalanche of boiling mud, towards the low-lying districts along the coast.

The violence of the eruption continued to increase. On 18 June, at a point higher up the fissure, a new crater burst open. Its lava, which was extremely fluid, poured unhindered down the already solidified surface of the previous torrent and, adding its impetus to the still moving lava ahead of it, advanced in a more dreadful flood than ever. Part of it poured in a tidal wave right up the top of a valley through which a tributary ran into the lake; the great mass of lava, however, reached the upper edge of a high waterfall and plunged over the precipice, a grandiose cataract of fire.

Very soon afterwards the burning fringe of the flood reached the sea.

The line of craters ceaselessly went on gushing out new waves of liquid basalt. From every side the molten stuff came trickling down the hills, filling the valleys, spreading a blanket of fire over the inhabited plains. Even before the torrents of lava reached them, hamlets, homesteads and farmlands were destroyed by floods of water and mud, caused by the sudden melting of the glaciers and the snow. The red-hot onslaught followed soon afterwards, swallowing up twenty or more villages.

But even this outburst had not exhausted the eruptive force. For two years to come the volcano went on vomiting out a fantastic quantity of magma, the total volume of which equalled that of Mont Blanc. Iceland lost a fifth of its population (10,000 persons), as well as four-fifths of its flocks of sheep and more than half its cattle, in all more than two hundred and fifty thousand head of livestock. These deaths were caused partly by the sudden floods, partly by the onrush of lava, partly by the showers of hot ashes that ruined the pastures, and finally also by the terrible famine that followed.

Most present-day volcanoes, that is to say, almost five hundred of the six hundred and twenty odd that are known, are to be found along the shores of the oceans: all round the Pacific, in the Lesser Antilles, the Southern Pacific Islands, and the East Indies. Their lava, which is much more viscous than that of the volcanoes just described, solidifies rapidly and so cannot spread over such large areas. This viscosity, due to the particular nature of the lava's chemical composition, tends to prevent the gases from percolating through the magma and escaping gradually. The result is that they accumulate under enormous pressure, till the moment when the pressure becomes greater than the resistance of the volcanic mass. Then comes the explosion, which is always violent and sometimes cataclysmic.

As examples of this type of eruption I may quote those of Merapi, Tomboro and Papandayan in Java, and above all the terrific explosion of Krakatoa, an island in the Sunda Straits, in 1883. The whole island was shattered to smithereens. The noise of the explosion was heard in Australia, more than two thousand five hundred miles away, and the vast cloud of volcanic dust flung up into the stratosphere travelled round the globe several times in the course of the following months, the first lap taking only thirteen days.

The news of this catastrophe rocked the world. Less than twenty years later the disaster in Martinique and the total destruction of the town of St. Pierre were to arouse even greater horror.

The story of St. Pierre is indeed a strange one, and is a good illustration of how blind human beings can be.

For a quarter of a century the people of this little port in the Windward Islands had been living tranquilly at the foot of Mount Pelée, paying little attention to the very faint wisps of steam sometimes floating at the mountain's peak. The memory of the 1851 eruption, which had not been particularly serious, was fading out of minds made all the more heedless by an agreeable climate. People were used to this volcano, which was, so to speak, part of the scenic background, and often used to go on excursions up its slopes in jolly little parties and had Sunday picnics on the rim of the crater—a five-mile climb up the grassy slopes and bluffs. That was the attitude of people of St. Pierre. There were thirty thousand of them, of whom about seven thousand were white.

About the middle of April 1902, it was noticed, without much anxiety being aroused, that the top of the mountain had begun smoking again. The plume of smoke became denser and steadily darker. Occasionally thicker clouds were sent rolling up, and the young people who found it more delightful than ever to go for picnics on the summit, attracted by curiosity about what was going on, reported muffled rumblings underground. Then these expeditions had to cease, because showers of fine ash were making it thoroughly unpleasant to linger on the edge of the cauldron. The rumblings became more noticeable, and the column of smoke grew bigger and ever blacker. People began to talk about 1851 again. . . . But in 1851 the town itself had not been in danger.

The animals were the first to show anxiety. They began to leave the slopes around the crater, and it was observed that reptiles, deserting the craggy fields of old lava, which were full of nooks and crannies, were beginning to invade the plantations and coming closer to the town, while swarms of migrating birds also avoided the region. Certain strange phenomena, furthermore, alarmed sailors: there were ground-swells in calm weather, and now and then the water suddenly became warm. . . . The rain of ash was falling more and more densely on the countryside, and after a while reached the town itself, while the wall of smoke continued to rise into the tropical sky, where sudden storms were constantly breaking out.

On May 5 a torrent of steaming mud, doubtless caused by an eruption of lava and ashes into the water of a little lake that had formed in the crater, came pouring down the hillside and overwhelmed a sugar-refinery, killing twenty-four people. Instantly refugees came crowding into St. Pierre, causing great alarm.

The situation was growing serious. What were the authorities going to do? They were chiefly preoccupied with the forthcoming elections. The main thing was that the electors should not leave before polling day . . . And so reassuring announcements were posted up, based on the opinion of a 'scientific commission', and proclamations were made, appealing to the population to keep their heads. The Governor-General, Mouttet, took his personal share in this campaign by coming from Fort-de-France, together with his wife, for the specific purpose of reassuring the more timorous. And so, in spite of bellowings that became louder every day, in spite of the sinister smoke lit up by sudden lightning-flashes, in spite of the clouds of ashes that the wind carried down on St. Pierre, only a very few people decided to leave. Entirely given up to political enthusiasm, the town lived out its last days in feverish activity.

Then the crater began to fling out incandescent lava. The ashes, expelled at the rate of tens of thousands of cubic feet per second, finally spread out in a black vault that hid the sun and came raining down ceaselessly over the whole countryside. While the town was thus being enveloped in a twilight that seemed to herald the end of the world, the rumblings grew terrifying. Soon they were mingled with tremendous explosions. For three days terror increased, driving people out into the streets, making them crowd into the churches or huddle together in the cellars. Then came a relative lull and once more they turned to their political concerns. It was over, they thought; the crisis was now past. It would be the same as in 1851. Crowds gathered round the reassuring posters. A few people left the town in carriages, others took ship for Fort-de-France or Guadeloupe, but ships were still coming into the port. Five miles from the city centre the great pillar of ebony was steadily growing thicker and taller, slashed across by incessant zigzags of thunder and lightning. Torrential downpours flooded the town.

In the night of 7–8 May the violence of the cataclysm continued to increase, and now panic broke out. From dawn onwards, thousands of men, women and children, white and coloured, instinctively made their way down to the sea, as the only way out, thronging the quays and the landing-stages. How many of them could find room on the twenty or so vessels riding at anchor in the roads? Now flames were shooting out of the mountain, and an unspeakable roaring had begun over the heads of this motionless, speechless throng.

A little before eight o'clock the force at work in the earth became silent, as though to let all these human beings have time to prepare themselves for death. Then suddenly, with a roar like the firing of thousands of huge guns, the summit of the mountain burst wide open and a wall of fire came rushing down the slopes at a tremendous speed.

Forty thousand people standing helpless, with the sea at their backs, saw this wall of fire coming straight at them. In three seconds it had reached the villas and the gardens of the fort. In one more second, St. Pierre had disappeared in a burning cloud. The compressed air which the avalanche drove ahead of it flung into the sea, in a solid mass, all that terrified humanity wedged together on the quays. An instant later the water of the harbour was boiling and, in an immense cloud of steam, the ships capsized and were swallowed by the sea, or blazed like torches.[1]

---

[1] Only two cargo-boats, the *Roddam* and the *Roraima*, escaped from the general wreckage, dreadfully damaged and with only a few survivors. 'The wave of fire,' Assistant Purser Thompson of the *Roraima* was later to recount, 'was on us and over us like a lightning flash. It was like a hurricane of fire. I saw it strike the cable steamship *Grappler* broadside on and capsize her. From end to end she burst into flames and then sank . . . The town vanished before our eyes . . . Captain Muggah was the only one on deck not killed outright. He was caught by the fire wave and terribly burned. He yelled to get up the anchor, but before two fathoms were heaved in the *Roraima* was

In the warehouses thousands of casks of rum exploded simultaneously, and this horrible punch ran in blazing streams down the burnt and blackened streets and poured away into the sea in flames.

Nothing was left of the tamarisks, those gaudy crimson flowers, of young girls in their loveliness, of plump childish flesh and wrinkled old men, of all the thoughts, cares, loves and quarrels, of officialdom or even the voting papers on which this fated town had recorded its pathetic, futile will. Of all this literally nothing remained. In the afternoon, while the volcano, still grumbling, seemed to be dropping off to sleep again, some sailors from the French cruiser *Suchet*, venturing into the caved-in streets where fires still raged, found three living beings, whom they pulled out from under the thick blanket of ashes, frightfully burnt. Two of them died almost at once, the third very soon afterwards. But in an underground cell in the prison an old Negro, guilty of heaven knows what peccadillo, had been locked up, and two or three days later his terrified cries for help reached the ears of the sailors who were still hunting through the ruins. So after all one human being did survive in the flesh to bear witness to the fact that St. Pierre had once existed.

St. Pierre was a town whose inhabitants all died in a single day—when they need not have died.

Volcanoes have caused many catastrophes, but those three fatal seconds in St. Pierre, after three weeks of reckless unconcern and three days when its people lived in an agony of dread, will undoubtedly remain the classic tragedy in the history of volcanic disasters. Like all tragedies, it

---

almost upset by the boiling whirlpool, and the fire wave had thrown her down on her beam ends to starboard. Captain Muggah was overcome by the flames. He fell unconscious from the bridge and fell overboard . . . Before the volcano burst, the landings of St. Pierre were covered with people. After the explosion not one living soul was seen on land.'

has a lesson for us. It is for men to turn this lesson to account in future.

There was also a scientific conclusion to be drawn from this cataclysm, which had had such surprising features. Experts rushed to Martinique, chief among them the celebrated geologist Lacroix, who stayed there for many months, studying the process of a form of eruption, which then was new to modern man: the burning cloud.

After the appalling outburst of May 8, the eruptive phase was not finished. In fits and starts 'burning clouds' continued to be emitted from the peak of Mount Pelée, and always in the same direction. Lacroix had installed his observatory on a relatively sheltered spur of the mountain, and was able to follow the mechanism of these phenomena and get a fairly good idea of their nature. Twenty-eight years later, a new, though less serious, stirring of the volcano was to give the great volcanologist Perret an opportunity to complete and perfect our knowledge of this particular form of activity, henceforth known as *the Peléean type*, the hot clouds of dust and steam being its essential characteristic. This is a flood of lava pulverised by the violence of the explosion, each particle of it, from the most minute to the largest, being surrounded by a sort of sheath of gas at a tremendously high temperature. One might speak of an *emulsion* of incandescent lava in burning gases. The presence of this gaseous skin, which eliminates practically all friction between the solid constituents, is what gives the avalanche its extraordinary mobility.

It is probable that the generation of such a burning cloud—a *horizontal* emission of lava and gas—is determined by a sudden rise in the temperature of the acidic and viscous magma, which is extremely rich in liquid gas. The critical point once passed, the liquid gases all at once separate into myriads of bubbles, each of which explodes. Nothing can resist the tension developed in this way; the side of the volcanic dome bursts or cracks, and the emulsified lava escapes, self-propelled by its instantaneous and repeated emission of these liquid gases. The cloud charges out horizontally, clearing gorges and valleys at a leap, then, under its own weight, pours down the hillside. Its exceptional mobility, combined with this self-propulsion, which can be compared to that of a rocket, enables it to get up the speed that terrified St. Pierre and engulfed it in the same instant.

The parties from the *Suchet* that visited the seared town everywhere saw bodies huddled up and generally stripped of their clothes by the breath of the fire. Some of these bodies were quite charred; others were almost intact; but all had their hands or arms over their mouths. The deduction made was that before being touched by the incandescent wall they had been asphyxiated by the stratum of gas and compressed air which the cloud drove ahead of itself.

This colossal discharge of energy is followed, in eruptions of the Peléean pattern, by an extremely curious phenomenon. This is the rearing up of a dome, a mass of rock that slowly grows up out of the crater. It seems probable that this dome is formed by the accumulation of thousands of little streams of the very acidic dacitic lava that has now lost its gas and is therefore extremely viscous. These streams have no sooner been ejected than they 'set' and cannot trickle any further. In a few months a volume of millions of cubic feet can be amassed in this way, and the vast cauldron is not only choked up with it, but is actually replaced by a large conic structure. And there—paradoxical indeed—is a volcano without a crater.

But there is something still more extraordinary. A colossal monolith gradually rises through an open fissure in the dome. Though its top ceaselessly crumbles and slips down in burning avalanches, nevertheless it still goes on gaining in height. After the catastrophe of 1902, this tower, growing at an average rate of thirty to forty feet a day, rose to a height of more than a thousand feet above the dome. This lava, which was viscous, had become gradually covered with a hard shell, while the interior of the ever

lengthening needle for a long time remained in a semi-
fluid state. Then, once the gases underneath stopped
pushing, the interior of the mighty column also cooled off,
the lava set and, as it did so, cracked and split. Blocks
broke loose and crashed down, the tip crumbled away,
and bit by bit the whole monolith split up and disinte-
grated. In another few months a pile of rubble was all
that was left of a sort of fantastic cathedral spire.

CHAPTER IV

THE BIRTH OF A VOLCANO

PAYA, sitting beside me in the front of the truck, did not say a word. But I could feel how wide awake and alert he was in his calm silence. In the world of darkness we were plunging deeper into all the time, the beam from the headlamps vaguely lit up, among tall clumps of pale grasses, the gleaming bright eyes of nightjars cowering close to the ground, flying away only at the very last second. Sometimes a furtive animal crossed the beam of light—a little antelope, a genet, or a stone-marten.

We had now gone eighty miles and the road for a short while ran along the glimmering lake; we were starting up the Makengere escarpment when the thunder of a distant storm became audible over the noise of the engine and the clatter of jolting metal. Storms are frequent at Kivu in this season.

'Let's hope it isn't raining where we're going,' I said to Paya, 'or else we shall have to sleep in the car.'

'Ndio, Bwana!' ('Yes, Master!'), Paya replied, everlastingly ready to agree, everlastingly good-tempered and placid.

It was over two years now since Paya and I had set up as a permanent team. We trusted each other. We were, as he said, *manaumé ya manaumé*, man and man. When I left Katanga, I had asked him if he would consider leaving

with me and going far away from his own people. The
Negroes are deeply devoted to their families, but they also
have a passion for travel. Paya did not hesitate. 'Ndio,
Bwana,' he had replied with his wise smile. And he had
at once sent his young wife and children back to his native
village, on the hot banks of the wide and muddy Lualaba.
Leaving for Kivu several days later, we had passed through
this *mukini* of mud huts with thatched roofs, and we had
made a brief stop for him to say goodbye to wife and
children, for it would be a year before he returned.

'Kwenda muzuri!' the woman and the little children
called out, stretching out their arms and waving the
palms of their hands towards us. ('A good journey!')

'Bakia muzuri,' Paya replied simply. ('A good homekeeping.')

Such was my Paya, with his broad dark face and flashing
smile, not much given to talking, a man to rely on.

As we were winding on our way up loop after loop of
the long stony climb, we suddenly looked at each other in
excitement. The sound of the thunder had not stopped
since we had noticed it for the first time. It seemed to me
that I could read a question in Paya's eyes—perhaps not
so much one he was asking me as one he was simply
putting to himself.

I stopped the vehicle. In the sudden silence, the growling
went on, its volume now increased, singularly distinct,
and with a steadiness which was surprising and gradually
became unnerving. It went on without interruption, far
away, very deep. I remembered artillery barrages. But
here was something bigger and heavier still, and as though
eternal.

The volcano!

The realisation shot up in each of us at the same instant.
In spite of the fact that I had been waiting for this for
the last two days, the effect was amazing. And yet the
noise came to us muffled by a distance of some thirty
miles. After a short interval of silence, in which, perhaps
for the first time, Paya and I shared the same obscure

feelings in the very depths of our being, I switched the engine on again.

A few minutes later, at the top of the last bend, we saw the darkness rent by an immense cone of fire. It was three times higher than it was wide, scarlet, and underlined, at the base, by a band of intense yellow.

Seen through binoculars, the sight was fantastic. I could make out the continual movement in the cone of fire, which was made up of myriads of incandescent particles being flung up without pause and then pursuing their course through the air. Some projectiles, which did not rise so high, doubtless because of being heavier, were still red-hot when they fell, and the dark sides of the volcanic cone were spattered with this fiery rain. Over the left-hand rim a wave of sparkling yellow came pouring out, shaken by occasional convulsions. The bush was on fire all round the volcano. And immense crimson serpents, streaked with thousands of orange stripes and spots, went scattering in all directions. . . .

It was clear from the start that the eruption was not from either Nyamlagira nor Niragongo: at the altitude we had reached now, which was no more than 6,500 feet, we were already higher than the volcano. I remembered then a trip I had taken into the Virunga mountains. Apart from the eight gigantic cones there were—and this had struck me at the time—hundreds of extinct volcanoes very much smaller in size. Whereas the former towered over the high plateau by five to ten thousand feet (as the Matterhorn towers over Zermatt, or Mont Blanc over Chamonix), the latter hardly looked more than little hills of about 150 to 1,000 feet. Recalling the existence of these little peaks dotted all over the district, I surmised that one of them must have wakened into life and that we were now watching a fresh outburst of activity on the part of one of these little 'cinder-cones', as they are called.[1]

[1] These little cones, which are very like the peaks known as *puys* in Auvergne, were formed, like them, by the accumulation of projectiles—bombs, scoriae, lapilli, ashes—vomited out of the crater, that is to say, without any piling up of streams of lava.

As it turned out, this first explanation, which occurred to me while I was still merely approaching the phenomenon, was not the right one. The fact is that no one has ever seen a cinder-cone come to life again, and it might almost be established as a law that these mechanisms become once and for all extinct after only a short life, which has generally lasted from several days to several months. What we were here witnessing, as I was soon to have proved to me, was the birth of a *new volcano* of the same type.

Saké, with all its agency offices, marks the northern extremity of Lake Kivu. Beyond it, the road goes over the lava flows from Nyamlagira. These flows have been cold and solid for a long time now, but in 1938 and 1939, after travelling more than twelve miles, cutting the old road and swallowing up a Protestant mission, they came right down into the waters of the lake. At that time, Saké was a little port nestling in the shelter of a bay. In a few days the lava filled up the bottom of the bay, leaving Saké on the edge of a pond which is now all that remains of what was once a harbour.

About two o'clock in the morning we pulled up, having covered 115 miles since we left Bukavu. There was a blood-red sky, and the northern sky-line was one gigantic conflagration, merging at its eastern limit with the terrific column of fire from the volcano. The enormous regular rumblings, punctuated by sharp explosions, greatly heightened the terrifying quality of the scene. Getting out of the truck, the three of us spent a long time simply looking at it, unable to gaze our fill. Tall, skinny Kaniepala, who had at last awakened, was still draped in his light-coloured blanket and looked like a spirit contemplating his own strange handiwork.

'Come on,' I said, 'let's get on with the job.'

We pitched our tent right by the edge of the road, and set out in the cool darkness of the night towards Mount

Rumoka. Lying between our camp and the district where
the eruption was going on, Rumoka struck me as a suitable observation post. It is one of the numerous little
cinder-cones of which I have spoken. About 300 feet in
height, it came to violent birth in 1912 and went out
after six weeks of extremely vigorous life.

We had to cross solidified flows of that very unusual lava,
limburgite. I don't know why such a rarity had to lie right
in our track! Its surface is made up of an indescribable
chaos of unsteady blocks of all shapes and sizes, slabs brittle
as glass, the smallest fragment of which bristles with sharp
needles. To our misfortune, we stumbled into this horror.
Paya had set out without shoes and, in spite of the horny
skin with which Nature had provided the soles of his feet,
he found the going pretty disagreeable. More and more
often he had to stop and, standing on one leg, with the
other drawn up, pull out fearsome jagged pieces. Then he
would hurry limping after me, and, in an apologetic voice,
beg: 'Tala, Bwana.' ('The lamp, Master.') At first I
directed the beam for him, but more than once I had
to get out my pocket-knife and help him dig out the
savage little jag.

'Go back to camp,' I said several times. 'I don't need
you.'

'Wapi, Bwana!' ('Get along with you, Master!') was
all the answer he would give, smiling his usual smile.

Not only was it Paya's feet that suffered! The palms
of our hands and our knees also served as pin-cushions for
these sharp needles, for we often lost our balance and
occasionally fell on all fours.

At first I swore between my teeth, in a low voice. In the
course of the second hour, my voice rose slightly higher
at each fall. The moment came when I yelled out a curse
in a voice that was nearly a match for the volcano itself.
In that very instant Paya stepped on a slab that was as
fragile and sharp as glass. There the two of us stayed, one
on all fours and the other up to his waist in knife-edged
debris, both scratched, bleeding and breathless, and

shouting with laughter, like two lunatics. We were both so utterly at the end of our tether, feeling just like children who had 'lost their way in the awful great forest', and so resented the thousands of traps all along our course, that finally we hit on the only healthy solution and suddenly saw the funny side of it.

'All the same, Paya, won't you admit this is better than being in the office at Bukavu?'

I was sure of his answer, for Paya loved nothing but the bush, however uncomfortable it was, and heartily despised all those 'advanced' persons who made scratches on bits of paper for their living. But his scorn became truly Olympian when its objects were those white officials who, being higher up in the hierarchy, could give orders to the European bush-dwellers. To him the thing seemed simply incomprehensible—grotesque! The mere idea of escaping from the annoyances of town life so delighted him that instead of extricating himself from his hole carefully, he leaned hard, with both hands, on the edge of the slab. The slab gave way, and Paya disappeared completely from sight.

After this rather peculiar breathing-space, we started out again, carefully. But the greater our caution the more our misfortunes seemed to increase. The steep crags gashed our shins, the brittle slices of glass multiplied under our feet, and we had more and more of such grievous semi-disappearances. . . . I had bound up one of my hands in a handkerchief, and had torn off the tail of my shirt to bandage the other.

Frankly, we had not fully appreciated what it meant to have to cross that petrographic rarity, limburgite.

Three hours' slow progress got us over rather more than a mile of bristling lava which separated us from the foot of Rumoka. By contrast, the climb up the cone was sheer pleasure. The slopes and gullies of lapilli[1] and volcanic sand into which we sank at every step, were as soft to us as sandhills by the sea.

[1] *See Appendix* I (a).

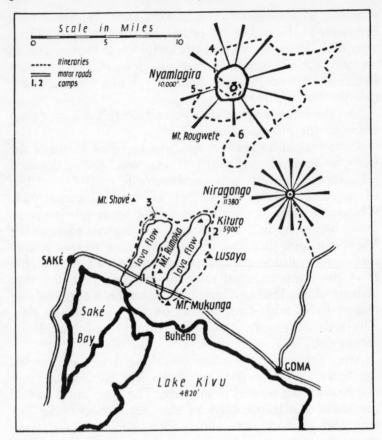

To make matters worse, all this misery was in vain. The observation-post showed us very little, beyond the fact— which I had guessed from the beginning—that there were two distinct vents, one to the east, roaring and gushing out that colossal cone of fire, and the other, closer to our point of vantage, to the west, from which there appeared to be a fairly 'quiet' outflow—if one can call it 'quiet' by any standards—of a great flood of lava. In contrast with the eastern centre of activity, with its deafening din, this one seemed almost silent. There were only some sporadic explosions, which sounded rather like anti-tank guns.

Starting from the first vent, an immense flood of lava was spreading out towards Lake Kivu. At least three miles long and about three-quarters of a mile wide, it was being fed by the continuous overflowing of the crater, sometimes faster, sometimes slower. As it flowed further away from its point of origin, this glaring yellow fluid turned gradually darker and darker red. Soon all that still showed up in the darkness were flecks and rays of incandescent matter sparkling out of fissures in the now dead crust.

Looking down on that vast expanse all glittering with thousands of points of light, I suddenly had a queer feeling that I was standing not in the heart of the African continent, gazing on a savage cataclysm, but on a hill overlooking some great industrial city in Europe. It was as if I were contemplating Liége by night, its windows all lit up, its factories with furnaces a-glare, its street-lamps strung out along the main thoroughfares—as if I were looking down on that from one of the hills that enclose the Meuse.

CHAPTER V

FIRST ROUND

THERE were a number of cars pulled up on the road. It was a mixed gathering, including a little jeep held together with pieces of wire, and a two-year-old sports car. In them were sightseers from Goma, or even from as far away as Coste. As is usual when old friends get together, there was a great deal of talk and bustle. It all seemed a little like a Sunday excursion, and a practical joker, recognising the tripperish atmosphere, had nailed a piece of cardboard to the trunk of a protea tree, announcing: 'Snacks served at any time.'

The advance fringe of the lava, we were told, was no more than a hundred, or at most a hundred and fifty yards away. People were going to see for themselves, following little tracks first trodden down in the bush by the wild animals, and already considerably widened by the sightseers of the last two days. Negroes offered to serve as guides to these parties. It was a fine chance for them to earn in half an hour what usually took them two days' hard work, and this without any trouble or danger, the lava's progress being very slow. Many of the whites were impressed enough to accept their services, so business was flourishing.

Going along the path I met a party of returning tourists. 'Hello! Be careful, don't go too close!'

Through the clusters of brambles and the tangles of branches and creepers one could by now see the bright blaze of the flaming trees. After twisting and turning among the thorny thickets, we suddenly found ourselves face to face with a sort of vast pile of burning coke, covered with a thin layer of grey. It was three to eight yards high, and was slowly advancing.

From time to time, under the continual pressure, a whole lump would break off and come crashing down, shattering into glowing blocks. Then for several seconds we could see into the glaring yellow interior of the torrent. Almost at once, however, the cooling of the surface dimmed the glow.

The front of the torrent, over half a mile wide, was progressing in distinct 'lobes', tongue after tongue licking out ahead. Sometimes one of them stopped for what seemed a long time, either because the lie of the land was obstructing its progress, or because the pressure from upstream had lessened momentarily. Occasionally one or other of the forward points began to move ahead much faster, up to a hundred yards a minute, as though the monster had lost patience and meant to drive the sightseers back.

As the wall of fire came closer, the vegetation dried up. The leaves shrivelled, the trunks cracked and split, and suddenly a bright flame would ripple through the trees and set them flaring away, roaring and crackling. But the biggest trees had no time to dry up before the magma touched them. A tomato-coloured tongue would creep out from under the mass of scoriae, reach the trunk, wrap itself round it, char the base, and then bring the whole tree tumbling down on to the bed of clinkers.

'Paya, tala tala.'

Tala tala was the glasses, in other words, the pyroscope, an instrument based on the principle that any black object heated to incandescence will take on a colour corresponding to its temperature. A filament is placed inside a lens, and, passing through a variable resistance, connected with an electric battery. A current, of varying intensity, can be passed through the filament, which will as a result turn red or yellow. The instrument is calibrated with precision, on the basis of incandescent substances at known temperatures. All I had to do was to focus the glasses on the lava and, switching on the current, adjust the resistance until the colour of the filament and that of the lava became identical.

A series of measurements taken in this way gave me an average temperature of 1,030 degrees centigrade for the hottest parts of the burning mass.

Nightfall sent the sightseers away. Next morning the lava had cut the road.

I was seething with desire to get near the craters. The western centre of activity, which was much less explosive than the other, seemed to me the more favourable for a first approach.

Leaving camp at dawn, we went round Rumoka to the north and walked in the direction from which the mighty bellowing was coming. Didn't Napoleon say one must 'walk straight up to the guns'?

'Well, Paya, no fear go fire-mountain?'

'Wapi, Bwana! Me no Banyabongo!'

The Banyabongo are the natives of this district. Descended from tribes decimated by the raids of Arab slave-traders, they had taken refuge in these mountainous districts (poor and cold for Negroes), and are a rather miserable-looking lot, by no means handsome. The other tribes tend to look down on them. As it happened, I had not been able to get a single one of them to act as guide for us.

'When shetanis [devils] wake up,' Paya said to me, 'men hereabouts no go into bush any more.'

'What did they tell you about it?'

'They say: devils wake up because wicked men no

make sacrifices. Devils·angry, throw fire-stones at men.
So they sacrifice goats. When shetanis very very angry,
they sacrifice cows.'

'Yes,' I commented, 'a good excuse for stuffing your-
selves at a big feast.'

'No, Bwana. Throw living goats *in* lava.'

We walked on for a time in silence, and then he resumed:

'Also they say, sometimes one sacrifice not enough
because when shetanis no more angry, then something
else.'

'Oh, indeed? And what's that?'

'Old great chief, him dead, sick in other world. He
jump about a lot in bed, turn over and over, *aaai*! And
earth open up . . .'

'So then more sacrifices than ever?'

'Yes, Bwana. Sacrifices not always do good, but never
do harm!'

And he began to laugh, showing all his splendid white
teeth.

This reminded me of a curious affair in connection with
sacrifices, the conclusion of which I had attended at
Katanga, in the southern Congo, more than six hundred
miles from here.

'Iko sawa sawa Katombi.' ('It's just like Katombi.')

'Kabisa, Bwana.' (Exactly.)

Katombi was an old chief, a tall, thin, dignified person
with noble features and a head of silvery hair. He reigned
over a large tribe in the Kibara mountains—till the day
when the administrative officer of the territory had him
arrested. This was in 1945, just at the time when I arrived
in this part of the world, and I was able to be present at
the first cross-examinations of this king and his leading
chieftains.

For many, many moons, on pretexts very similar to
those which here brought about the death of a goat or a
cow, he had been ordering the sacrifice of human beings.
In this case his ancestor's anger was making itself felt not
by means of volcanic phenomena, but by the ills with

which, in their annoyance, they visited Katombi himself. And so, in order to get rid of dysentry or toothache, he would have some unhappy wretch brought to him—man, woman or child, whichever his 'hunters' happened to light on. He had a whole team of these hunters, and whenever need arose they went out to catch a victim in some other tribe's village or in the bush, if anyone should have had the bad luck to venture there alone. Once caught, their man's feet and hands were bound together with a single rope; a stick was passed through them and shouldered by two men, and the hunting-party set out at a regular jog-trot back to the village, with the human being slung in the same way as an antelope. Finally the victim was slaughtered according to a ritual ceremony and his blood sprinkled on a fetish. Among the evidence for the prosecution which the administrative officer had collected in the clay hut that served him for an office, I saw a little wooden statuette, about a foot in height, blackened both by age and by layer upon layer of dried blood.

Last of all, the victim's head was cut off. While it was still warm, Katombi grabbed the head and, holding it between his long, slender hands, gazed into its face, afterwards pressing it against his cheek or the top of his head or to his belly, in order to deaden the pain.

'And do you think it worked, Paya?'

'Wapi, Bwana!' ('Get along with you!')

'But then why all these sacrifices?'

'Don't know. Perhaps he forget pain when he see man suffer more than him. Perhaps too they eat killed man.'

We were advancing very slowly over ground that was made up of solidified old lava, riddled with crevasses and holes hidden by the scrub. We spent the whole day fighting our way through this thorny jungle. Towards the middle of the afternoon we came out on the magnificent cliff formed by a lava flow, a wall of scoriae piled up to a height of about thirty feet. The lava was moving on very slowly, indeed almost imperceptibly. Only the incessant crumbling

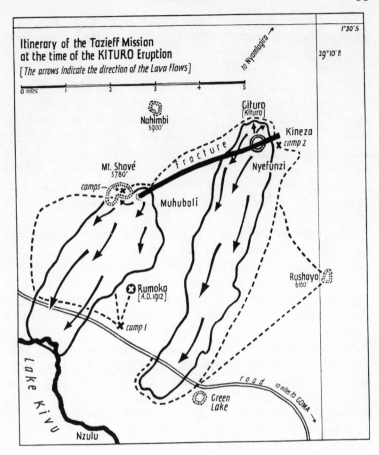

Itinerary of the Tazieff Mission
at the time of the KITURO Eruption
[The arrows indicate the direction of the Lava flows]

off of chunks of slag betrayed the fact that it was in cease-less motion.

This hot, grumbling wall, the sides of which were con-tinually sending up plumes of steam and little eddies of grey smoky fumes, formed an impenetrable obstacle to our further progress towards the volcano. There was nothing for it but to retreat.

Back at camp, we were somewhat consoled by the goat stew that Kaniepala had had all this time to concoct for us.

We returned to the attack the next day, still, unfortunately, without a guide. But I was quite happy, for I had received a ciné-camera from Bukavu and was in a hurry to get some sensational shots if I could.

The boy who had brought me this camera was a very brave and hardy Warega, thin and lithe, who at once agreed to go with us. Leaving Kaniepala, as usual, to look after things at the camp, the three of us set out on a long detour round by the west and north. I was hoping to reach the active vents of the volcano by taking the way round the foot of Mont Shové, an extinct cinder-cone which I had decided must be fairly near to our objective.

The extremely fine dust, which the violent explosions in the eastern crater were flinging out to a great height, caused condensation of the water-vapour in the atmosphere, which is always very abundant in equatorial regions, and big dark clouds, forming again and again, burst over our heads, producing torrential downpours. We were soaked right from the start.

Setting our course by the compass, we worked our way through the dripping jungle. Sometimes a wide, well-trodden elephant-track gave us a chance to gain some ground easily. Then it would go off in the wrong direction, or the clear track would split up into several paths and fade out. Once again the machetes would come into play, hacking through the brambles and creepers and the tangled branches of fallen trees. Step by step, hour after hour, slashing away, we cut our road ahead. It was a narrow, difficult trail, where we went in single file, clambering across tree-trunks and stumbling over blocks of basalt. Prickly plants of every kind scratched our arms and legs till they bled.

The British in East Africa have a delightful name for a particularly exasperating variety of plant, which is armed with strong, hooked thorns that take a merciless hold on your clothes or your flesh. It is 'wait-a-bit.' And there is nothing else to do, in fact, but stop and quietly unhook yourself—losing your temper infallibly means a proportionate increase in the degree of entanglement—and then start off, again as carefully as possible. 'Wait-a-bit' is a plant that is a great inculcator of patience and wisdom.

In the hostile, soaking jungle we moved on slowly and in silence, our horizon bounded only a few yards away by a curtain of branches and leaves. The rain streamed down on my head and in my face. I envied Paya and the Warega their thick mop of hair, on which the rain collected until they gave a sharp jerk of the head and shook it off, as a dog does coming out of a river. I, poor semi-bald white man, had the water trickling all over my skull, coming over my forehead in sheets, and gathering in my eyebrows, where it formed little reservoirs, which after a while overflowed and flooded my eyes. Another stream went down the bridge of my nose (broken in the course of my boxing activities), and I amused myself by emitting a puff of breath every five seconds or so, pulverising the drop that had been swelling and trembling on the tip of my nose.

The hours passed. Nothing but the bush, the bush, and the rain . . . At noon, after having been on the march since dawn, we still had got nowhere.

Suddenly the forest came to an end, revealing the low, grey ceiling of clouds. We had come out on an enormous stony embankment, the edge of a big lava-flow.

The brownish barrier towered over us, about as high as a three-storeyed house. Without pause, pebbles of scoriae rolled down to the bottom of the gigantic pile, making a faint clatter like crockery being smashed. The fine rain vapourised as it came into contact with the burning blocks. And this warm mist, which was continually being increased by the steadiness of the downpour, added its stifling heat to the ordinary suffocating quality of the equatorial climate in the rainy season.

On the left we could hear sharp detonations—fairly close, it seemed to me. The vents! From time to time this sound was mingled with a sort of infuriated whistling, doubtless to be accounted for by gases escaping under pressure.

A wedge of this surface slag broke off and the infernal substance stretched.

'Mafi ya bongo,' Paya murmured. ('Excrement of God.')

Warily, we moved along the edge of the flow, climbing towards its source. With that gloomy wall towering over us, we advanced in the direction of the noise.

Here the lava had burnt up the bush, clearing a way for us by destroying the thousands of hooked and clawed obstacles that had held us up for such a long time. There was no more need to cut through anything; we only had to watch our steps to make sure we did not stumble over tree-trunks or blocks. Some minutes of this more rapid, but still wary march, brought us to an indescribable entanglement barring our road: undermined by the lava, three huge trees had crashed down, their leafy crowns interlacing. I tried to get round this jumble to the left, but there I was stopped by a deep natural ditch (a frequent phenomenon in such a chaos of old lava), all running wild with stinging brambles. On the right the burning wall blocked the way. There was nothing for it but to blaze a trail straight ahead.

'Go to it, boy!'

Our Warega set about hacking a passage through the branches, while I turned the halt to account by getting the camera out of its case and beginning to film the wall of scarlet magma, that glaring cliff-face suddenly laid bare by the crumbling away of a mass of scoriae. This was the first time I had used a ciné-camera, and this red was very tempting for a colour-film.

I had been 'shooting' for no more than a few seconds when through the view-finder I saw the incandescent face of the wall swelling from the afflux of new material.

Suddenly it thrust out a huge protuberance, which stretched further in a tongue of viscous fire. It lengthened, grew bloated, and began to drive straight at us . . . After a second's stupefaction I realised what was happening.

Fighting down our excitement, Paya and I stopped to put the camera back carefully into its case.

'Run for it! *Toka!* Run like hell!'

With great swinging blows of their machetes the two natives flung themselves on the bush that barred our way. But the blunted blades would no longer cut through the elastic twigs, which slid away under the blows. My two companions stopped. Their arms hung inert, the whites of their eyes widened. Their faces had become queerly grey. Appalled to the point of speechlessness, they abandoned themselves to the supernatural power that was demanding their death. As for me, I felt no resignation at all, but a sudden terror strangling me with something like nausea and a will to survive which no hostile divinity could annihilate.

'Leta Kisu!'

I grabbed Paya's machete and began hitting away for all I was worth at the brambles and creepers, which I seized by the fistful in my left hand. I gasped and panted, as I bashed away at it. And I was afraid. And there was this banging and beating, and the brambles giving way, and the moving forward, forward . . . But the lava was coming forward all the time too! Its fiery breath was scorching our bare calves.

The Warega boy began chopping again beside me. Seeing that we had not been swallowed up on the spot, my two boys had regained hope. Side by side, tense, silent, the Warega and I lashed away at the jungle. Our hands were bleeding, our shoulders aching. It was slow as a nightmare. The lava was gaining on us. The burning of our legs, backs, and the nape of our necks was becoming unbearable.

'Ha!'

It was a wild groan of relief. For here was a space where

the vegetation was not so dense and we could gain a bit of ground. But the scrub that followed, and which there was no way round, seemed almost impenetrable. Paya took his machete from me again and set to work, with great flailing sweeps of his arm. The sturdy Warega at his side never for an instant stopped his heart-breaking work of felling the brambles. Fear, which for a moment had loosened its grip, now had a tight hold on us again. Foot by foot we advanced into the scrub. From second to second the heat increased, and all around us the leaves were shrivelling, curling up and crackling like paper. The slowness was torture. Once again I felt the burning on my calves, and now it was becoming steadily worse.

For God's sake, why did I ever come to this damnable country? A fine fool I must look, here behind these two 'boys', slashing away as hard as they can. With my belly I push against the Warega in front, my back arching in the attempt to get away from the heat, to gain even an inch on the torrid breath that is already roasting me. Now that I am no longer doing anything, now that I depend on the two others to carry our flight on, inch by inch, I have time, unfortunately, to think about myself, and I cannot help realising that I must cut a grotesque figure, with my hands running up and down from my calves to my buttocks, from the back of my neck down to my thighs, trying to protect the back of my body from that implacable radiation. The hairs on the backs of my legs are already toasted. I can smell scorching in my nostrils and confirm the impression by touch. I squash myself up against the Negro's back and push, like someone rude in a queue . . .

At last! We burst through that frightful obstacle of jumbled-up branches. Frantic, we race across some thinner undergrowth, leaping over obstacles and flinging ourselves, sobbing with breathlessness, on the top of a heaven-sent hillock—exhausted, drenched as much in sweat as from the rain.

Thirty paces behind us, with a great crackling roar, the scrub suddenly goes up in flames, like an enormous twist of straw.

Darkness had fallen long before we got back to camp, after almost fourteen hours of solid trudging through the heavy rain.

What a state we were in! My watch, which had gone perfectly well up to then, had stopped, being full of water. And water had got into my binoculars too, flooding the space between the eye-pieces and the object lenses.

The dry interior of the tent was sweet to me as any home regained. In the gentle light of the candles I gave myself up to the pleasure of relaxing in comfort. I spent a long time drying myself, rubbing myself down with dry towels, and then getting into dry clothes. So much dryness seemed miraculous. After a substantial meal all three of us gulped down several brimming glasses of grog, and even though he had been tucked away here safe and sound all day, Kaniepala did not need much urging to join us.

The effects of these drinks got me up about three o'clock in the morning.

I had hardly set foot outside the tent, still half asleep, when I felt that something out of the ordinary was happening. Then, with a leap, my brain came right out of its mists. The thing was—whereas in the preceding nights the glow in the sky had stretched from the north-west to the north-east, at an angle of about eighty degrees, now the lurid crimson had suddenly spread all over the west. Here was a real catastrophe! One lava flow, pouring out of those western vents that we had got so near to the preceding day, threatened to cut the road behind us leading back to Saké—our only route of retreat, since the road to Goma was already blocked.

Yelling at the top of my voice, I woke the boys.

'Paya! Kaniepala! Mbio!' ('Quick!')

In record time camp was struck and all our equipment piled up on the truck. The two negroes jumped on even as I drove off.

Ahead of us the sky was raving red. As though our four combined wills were urging it on, the truck plunged down the track, starting off on a neck-and-neck race with the monster.

This was not kept up for long. Soon we saw, at the end of a straight stretch, a wall of fire making further progress impossible. Switching off the engine, I let the truck coast on down. We stopped ten yards away from a glaring red cliff of lava with flashes of blinding yellow lightning shooting out of it, the whole thing roaring like a distant waterfall. On each side of the road was the rustling roar of flames from the bush, which was all on fire. We were silent, faced with this gigantic conflagration.

This flow had come down a great deal faster than the first, the one that had already cut the road further to the east, at the beginning of the eruption. In the last ten hours it had covered something like three miles, and the glare in the sky on our left told us that it was advancing towards the lake.

I considered our position. There was only one hope of escape short of swimming for it, and this was that the first flow, four miles to eastward, which had cut us off from Goma and seemed to have been slowing up during the last three days, might not yet have reached the shore of the lake. In that case we could try to get round in front of it and reach the safe slopes of Mount Mukunga.

Turning our backs on the incandescent wall, we therefore drove at full speed eastward and did not stop till we reached the high bank—now cold and dark—of the first torrent of lava. Then each of us loaded up with as much of the baggage as he could carry. Instruments, film, and books were all taken, but there was no help for it, we had to abandon the heavy equipment and the truck itself.

Making our way more or less straight along the edge of the lava, almost all the time hacking our way through the scrub, we marched on in single file towards the south. In us—or in me, at any rate—there was still the haunting fear that we might be too late and find our retreat already cut off . . .

Those were long hours, and the rain was coming down again, too.

A little after dawn, we began to swing our course over to the east. The lava, every time we came on it in clearings in the bush, seemed solid, the fire all gone out of it. Our hopes grew.

At last we came out of the forest, which was not so thick in this place, and struck out across the maize fields and the vast banana-plantations that slope away up towards the steep sides of Mount Mukunga.

CHAPTER VI

SECOND ROUND

LIKE an inexperienced young boxer who has taken on an old-timer with the gloves, I had got a thorough beating right from the beginning of my tussle with the volcano. This was what came of not knowing the job! Completely winded, I had gone back to my corner and was collecting myself for the next round.

My 'corner' was the plantation belonging to my friends the de Muncks, on the edge of the lake, where we had found a delightful refuge after the thrills of that unforgettable night. Hospitality is the ordinary and expected thing among the up-country Europeans, but the hospitality of Adrien and Alyette de Munck is so big-hearted that it has become proverbial.

Thanks to them—for, having been established in this district for more than twenty years, they were adepts in persuading the natives to do what they wanted—I was at last able to get porters who were willing to face the red devils. My host and hostess themselves were far from lacking in nerve: solid, easy-going Adrien and his valiant wife were resolved to accompany me on my new attempt.

Both the lava flows had followed a course between their plantation, Buheno, and the western centre of activity, which I had vainly tried to reach. Our caravan therefore steered, naturally enough, for the other vent, which, being explosive, was much more spectacular.

The Belgian Congo volcanoes Muhavura and Gahinga mark the frontier between Ruanda and Uganda. (*Congopresse*)

Kituro in eruption, a new volcano created in 1948 near Lake Kivu.

(*Congopresse*)

This antelope was asphyxiated by Kituro's volcanic gases, and later eaten by beasts of prey. (*Congopresse*)

The white plume of Kituro. (*Tazieff—Congopresse*)

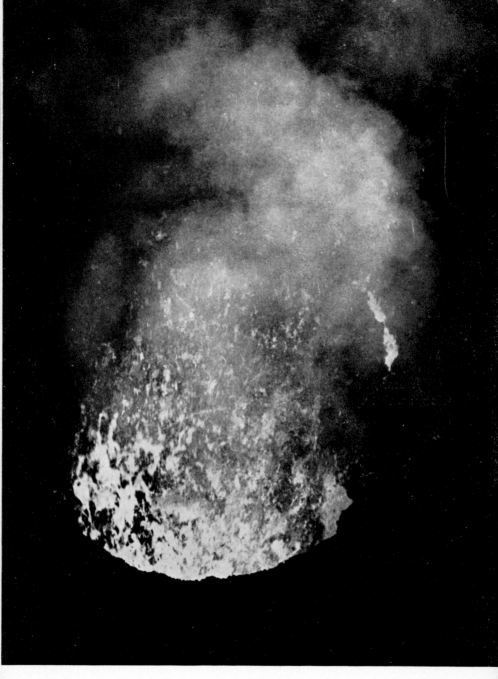

The mouth of Kituro, about 60 feet in diameter, taken at close range.
(*Tazieff—Congopresse*)

A flow of corded lava from Kituro. (*Tazieff—Congopresse*)
Below, another typical specimen of corded lava. (*Tazieff—Congopresse*)

A river of new lava moving across older flows. Kituro, 1948. (*Tazieff—Congopresse*)
The picture below, taken less than 15 feet away, shows lava moving at three miles
an hour, and at 1100° centigrade. (*Tazieff—Congopresse*)

An accumulation of roped and smooth lava from the Kituro eruption of 1948.

(*Tazieff—Congopresse*)

A good track, trodden out by the bare feet of the natives and the trampling of cows, led to the village of Lusayo, perched in the midst of its banana-plantations on the summit of a little cinder-cone. From here on the track was not so clear, soon degenerating into no more than an elephant-spoor, and this led us to a pond formed by the heavy rain. In this region of porous lava, where every rainfall is at once absorbed before any stream can form, this pool was such an exceptional godsend that we pitched camp near to it, in a pleasant grassy clearing. I had wasted precious days in trying to reach the goal of my mission without help. Today three hours' journey had brought us into the immediate neighbourhood of the volcano.

There it was, quite close. . . . With a terrific din, its gigantic eruptive jet of reddish-tinged blocks shot up to a height of more than three hundred feet, gradually thinning out, then disintegrating and falling back in a thick, blackish shower. These blocks came down in such close concentration that in less than ten days a new cone, one hundred and fifty feet high, had piled up in a place where previously there had been nothing but a wooded valley.

We kept on along the edge of this valley, being always several fathoms above it. Between us and the volcano lay five or six acres of leafless trees that would have looked completely dead if it had not been for a few scorched leaves clinging, here and there, to the twigs. As we could not see, from where we were, either the foot of the cone or the torrents of lava, we went further northwards across a little savannah, then across a tongue of forest, and came out in a long ditch that had recently been torn open by the cataclysm. Here all the trees, uprooted or broken, were lying scattered about on a bed of light scoriae. The clearing, which was about twenty paces wide, wound away to the left; several hundred yards away, right in the axis of the fissure, the truncated cone rose up in all its roaring grandeur, with its mighty crimson plume floating over it. Every now and again there was a relative lull, and this unexpected calm seemed almost more threatening than the upheaval. It was as though some terrible beast had paused to regain breath before making another onslaught.

We walked on a little further, till we reached the zone where the lapilli were raining down. At that stage we were still too inexperienced to risk venturing further. Standing quite still, heedless of the passing of time, we stood staring at the extraordinary sight.

The lava, ceaselessly spurting up again and again, formed a thick incandescent column hovering permanently over the crater. Spent projectiles kept dropping out of this liquid pillar from points all up its height and falling back slowly, so that one saw a sort of sinister dark snow everlastingly falling against the red background of the rising mass. Spellbound, we watched these continually flying projectiles rise and fall in a fantastic fountain of white-hot rock, accompanied by the gun-roar of the explosions, with occasional irregular detonations breaking into the monotonous mighty growl. Above these terrible gambols the smoke grew denser, forming black clouds with livid gleams in them, lit up by the crimson glare from the crater itself.

THE GREAT FRACTURE

The long cutting that we had just discovered, strewn with uprooted trees, must date from the moment the eruption began.

Turning our backs to the volcano, we followed the fracture for several hundred yards to the east. It ran in an absolutely straight line, west by a few degrees south. Its width scarcely varied. All along it there was a not very thick blanket of blue-black scoriae, which squeaked under our feet. In the middle a crevasse gaped open, running from one end of this strange avenue to the other. In some places the distance between its edges was nearly as much as six feet, in others it was partly filled up by the crumbling of its edges, while elsewhere it had been sealed off by the flow of lava, now completely cold and hard, which it had itself emitted.

'That must have gone off with quite a crack when it split open!'

'Now I understand!' Alyette exclaimed. 'Everything on the shelves at Buheno came tumbling down!'

Adrien gave a great guffaw. 'It was four o'clock in the morning. Not the sort of time when we usually get up! But this certainly got us out of bed at record speed, and out of the house too! All the natives had come out of their huts by then.'

'And what happened?'

'What happened? Why, nothing! Alyette put all the things that had fallen down back into place and had the mess swept away. As for me, I went back to bed.'

That short and violent seismic tremor had been felt only within a radius of fifteen to twenty miles. Beyond that, nobody had noticed it.

That is actually one of the characteristic features of volcanic earthquakes: as they are produced near the surface of the earth, the shock, however violent, cannot continue very far.

The tremor felt at Buheno was caused by the abrupt opening of this fissure, along the edges of which we were so tranquilly pottering today. When the resistance of the surface of the earth's crust had been exceeded by the pressure of the magma rising out of the depths, the crust had split, or rather, cracked, and the waves of this sudden shock had sent the crockery flying off shelves, and awakened people, ten miles away.

'What day was it?' I asked, conscientiously pulling out my notebook.

'February 29th,' Adrien said. 'It takes a leap-year to produce that sort of practical joke!'

After that shock, utterly normal calm had prevailed at Buheno until the middle of the following night. Then, however, an appalling roar had once again brought people leaping out of their beds. And, standing on their doorsteps, whites and natives alike had seen rising up into the night sky, which was all aglare with it, the column of fire that came gushing out of the new-born volcano, accompanied by a sound like thunder. In other words, it had taken the magma twenty-four hours to rise to the top of the fault that it had forced open.

Nearly three-quarters of a mile to the east, we discovered that the big fracture branched out and formed a sort of cross-connection of many smaller fractures, like arteries.

To the west it led straight to the crater of the volcano which it had produced. Later I was to realise that it went on further, beyond the vent itself, to a distance of about four miles, right to the second vent—the non-explosive, merely effusive vent which I had vainly tried to reach at the beginning of my explorations. We were in fact dealing with an eruption of the 'fissure' type, recalling, though on a less tremendous scale, that which ravaged Iceland in the eighteenth century.

What tensions, increasing for years on end, what sudden readjustment of a balance that had gradually been shifting, had been necessary to cause such a break in the crust of the earth?

For a long time it was believed that within its external crust the earth consisted of a globe of liquid fire under pressure, volcanoes being the safety-valves of that colossal boiler.

Nowadays it is admitted that under a thin crystalline shell, forty to fifty miles thick, the interior of our planet is far from being liquid, at least in the sense in which we usually understand the term. This conclusion is the result of very detailed study of the behaviour of these seismic waves, which ripple out all round a deep centre, causing earthquakes and which, after sometimes going through the whole thickness of the globe, reach the observatories dotted about on its surface.

This study had revealed certain curious properties of magma. On a small scale it is solid; on a large scale it is fluid. Like the ice which to us seems solid, although it flows down the slopes of mountains or polar ice caps, deep magma can flow in currents. Convection currents, consisting of cells, may arise in its bowels.[1]

You must accept the idea that in certain regions of our planet these currents are more active than in others, and that they are, relatively speaking, very rapid (it is believed possible that they get up a speed of as much as twenty inches per year) under the earth's crust, down where more or less horizontal fluxes go out from the centre of a cell to its periphery—from its centre, which is rising, to its exterior, which is sinking. You must also think of the fantastic viscosity that makes this 'liquid', so long as it remains subject to the pressure there is in the depths, incredibly much more rigid than steel at our ordinary temperature. From all this you can deduce something about the strength of the forces produced by these currents, and the pressure they bring to bear on the underside of the earth's shell.

If this shell, which, compared with the size of the globe as a whole, is no thicker than the shell of an egg, is subject to such tensions, 60,000 to 120,000 pounds per square inch, it is not surprising that it has a tendency to stretch and then, when the strain exceeds the limit of its elasticity, to crack. It is in this way that those tremendous networks of faults are produced which sometimes scar whole continents. Such are the fractures that separated Arabia from Africa and—the waters of the ocean invading the space thus flung open—caused the birth of the Red Sea, which is sprinkled with volcanic islands and also has volcanoes along its shores. Networks of this kind cross-hatch the floor of the Pacific Ocean, and it is on them that there have been thrust up those great strings of volcanic islands, Hawaii, Samoa, Tuamotu, the Marquises, and yet other chains of islands in that vast ocean. There are also huge gashes in the Atlantic, scattered with volcanic vents: Jan Mayen, Iceland, Teneriffe, Ascension Island, Saint Helena . . . Analogous phenomena are to be found in Manchuria,

[1] *See Appendix* II (b).

in the South Seas, and in the Antarctic, and it is the same across the African continent, where volcanoes were born of those great sink-holes produced by the movement of parallel faults—enormous and famous valleys like the Great Rift Valley in the east and, further west, the Graben of the Great Lakes.

It is in this Graben, in the Great Lakes district, that our Virunga mountains stand. Their rising up was caused by more or less perpendicular faults, resecting the Graben faults, which run more or less north-east.

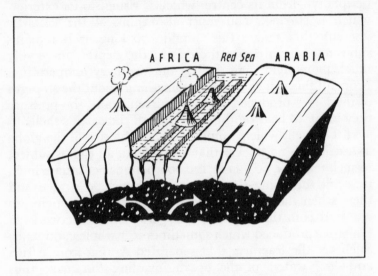

At the points where these fractures intersect, the deep magma, under terrific pressure from below, rises steadily towards the upper world. In proportion as it rises, the weight that is trying to hold it down gradually becomes less. This allows the many gases, present in fluid form in this strange liquid, to begin separating. The process speeds up. The external pressure decreases, the gases re-form, thus making the magma more fluid and hence also accelerating the rate at which it rises; the pressure on the magma decreases faster and faster, and there is a more and more marked separation of the gases, whose internal

tension is ceaselessly increasing. The magma by this time
has come through the inner crust and is nearing the surface
of the earth. The gases have now become separate, in the
form of bubbles, so making the magma lighter. Soon they
will make it effervescent. Their action is precisely that of
the carbonic acid that is crudely dissolved in a bottle of
beer and which, the moment the stopper is removed—that
is to say, when the external pressure is reduced—foams
to the surface and escapes. On the last lap—let us say in
the last fifty to a hundred feet—of its journey upward,
as a result of the pressure being removed almost entirely,
the magma rapidly passes to the liquid state. And
finally it gushes to the surface. It is then what we
call 'lava'.

The eruption will be more tumultuous or less according
to the quantity of gas present in the lava gushing out.
The fluidity of the lava will, on the other hand, be directly
related to its chemical composition. It may be as viscous
as molten glass, but it may come pouring out like boiling
pitch. The overflowing of lava can best be compared with
opening a bottle of champagne. It is no use looking through
the bottle while it is still corked: you will not see the slightest
trace of the presence of the gases. But the very instant
you pull out the cork, they appear and escape with such
force that they take with them some of the liquid contents
of the bottle, the amount ejected being greater or less
according to the violence of the expansion of the gases.
It is the same with lava: it gushes out as long as the gases
in it are pulling it along with them, or as long as other
gaseous elements, given off by the lower parts of the magma,
are still driving it upward. After this—if its chemical composition permits—since it is now too poor in volatile
elements to spread out any further, it remains simmering
in the depths of the crater.

One might therefore say that these deep convection
currents are the initial cause of the magma's rising and
that the gases are the essential motor of the volcanic
phenomenon in the strict sense.

When new fractures allow the magma to reach the surface of the earth at a new point, a volcano is born. Ordinarily, a volcano goes on living and developing over thousands of years. Sometimes, as we have seen, this includes dormant periods, which may be very long. Sometimes there are almost no dormant periods.[1] Now, it is possible that the result of the forces caused by these currents is the appearance of less extensive new cracks, which in the depths graft on to the major fractures that feed the great permanent volcanoes. The magma thus finds a way to drain out and pour over the surface, giving rise to a new volcano. Once the eruption is over, such secondary cracks are completely clogged up and extinct for ever. This is the case with the *puys* of Auvergne, and it is also the case with those hundreds of little cinder-cones scattered over the gigantic sides of Mount Etna, and over the volcanic fields of the Virunga Range. They are black hills, sometimes spotted with reddish or yellow trails of salts deposited by the volcanic gases, conical heaps of scoriae from fifty to hundreds of feet high, the summit containing the shallow cup of a crater that is now stopped up once and for all.

The deep convection currents seemed a possible cause of this four- or five-mile fissure, the violent opening of which had been emphasised by the earthquake on the night of 29 February. But, to judge by its appearance, the volcanic activity had been far from uniform along its length. This difference in the degree of activity was probably due to unequal localisation of the gases originally solvent in the magma and liberated during its ascent. While at this very moment they were still roaring away there behind us, gushing up out of the crater in a spectacular

---

[1] These variations in activity may be attributed to two categories of major causes: the convection currents and the chemical nature of the magma. It is also established that the astronomic position has its influence.

paroxysm, here everything had once more become calm
and silent. Some slowly curling fumeroles were still
being exhaled through little scattered vents. But that was
really all. Nevertheless, here too there had been activity
as violent as it was brief; it had left its traces in hundreds
of trees furiously wrenched up by the roots, as well as in
the light blanket of creaking scoriae through which we were
wading. They had gushed up in the form of balls of liquid
lava, bubbles flung into the air by the explosion of the
gases, and had set in the shape of these fragile fragments,
riddled with air-holes, bluish-black in colour, sometimes
iridescent, and heaped up twelve inches thick for a hundred
yards and more from the lips of the fissure.

On the first trees in the clearing hung shreds of now
congealed lava which at the time of their descent through
the air had still had the consistency of soft paste; they
dangled from the withered branches like old rags. The
amazing rapidity with which the surface of the lava cooled
off was evident to us here. At the moment it fell in its
pasty state, the lava must still have had a temperature of
more than nine hundred degrees centigrade. And yet it
had not maintained that high temperature long enough
to set fire to the twigs—many of which were not as thick
as a finger—to which they were now glued. The wood had
been scorched all round to a depth of about two millimetres, but the inside of the twig had suffered nothing
worse than total desiccation.

The following week I came back with the two de Muncks
to examine this portion of the fissure. Two Czech travellers,
going round the world in a sports car and writing up their
experiences for newspapers, had stopped at Buheno after
crossing Ethiopia, the Sudan and Kenya, and leapt at the
chance of joining our party. These two great gangling
fellows, one tall and dark, the other a giant with curly
fair hair, turned out to be delightful companions.

The party had strung out in the long clearing, each
person observing details on his own account. At the bottom
of a hole about six feet deep I had discovered some beautiful

orange-yellow crystals deposited by the volcanic gases. I
slid down into the pit in order to take some specimens.

I had scarcely touched the bottom with my toes when
I had a strange sensation of collapsing, giving way first
at the knees, then at the hips, and finally at the shoulders,
as if I were folding up like an accordion. My last sensation
was that of a strong hand seizing me by the collar. Then—
then I found myself lying on my back, staring up into a
sky against which I saw startled faces.

'Well, well, my friend!' I heard Adrien saying in cheerful
tones that were nevertheless a little shaken.

After we had been scattered in all directions for a good
quarter of an hour, a miraculous fluke at the critical
moment had brought one of the Czechs to the edge of the
hole where I was in process of losing consciousness, and
it was his strong arm that had hauled me out. So it was
that I learned to be on my guard against the carbon
dioxide that slyly lurks at the bottom of certain volcanic
depressions.

These Czechs were not the only strangers who had been
attracted to this place since the eruption. I also made the
acquaintance of a fifty-year-old geologist who was a
professor at the University of Johannesburg, and whose
misadventure is a story worth the telling.

A thorough expert in volcanology, he had set off by
plane at the first news of the eruption. Johannesburg is
three days' journey from Goma by air—not exactly next
door, you might say. Now, the Kivu volcanoes happen to
be within the limits of the Albert National Park, and in
order to visit them it is necessary to pay for a pass, which
can be got from any of the hotelkeepers in Goma. As our
excellent professor was buying his ticket, he met the Conservator, the big white chief of the Park in person. 'What
a godsend!' he thought to himself. 'Here's the very man
who will help me to get together the porters I need, and

I'll get straight from the horse's mouth the information I need about the early stages of the phenomenon.' Alas! Poor Professor Gevers was sadly mistaken! The fact was that whereas any Tom, Dick or Harry, whether planter, colonial administrator, store-keeper, tourist or gentleman of leisure living in retirement, by paying a merely nominal fee, had the right to enter within the—for that matter entirely fictitious—limits of the National Park and approach the volcano as closely as his personal daring would permit, our friend the expert discovered that there was an absolute veto on any geologist not accredited at the Institute of the National Parks, and worse still if he had the bad luck to be a foreigner. Nothing had the slightest effect—neither Gevers's high scientific standing nor the letter of recommendation written by the Governor-General himself. The eruption, having gushed up at that particular spot, happened to be the strictly private property of the Park—and of its Conservator.

A few days earlier, another geologist well-known throughout Africa, A. D. Combe, who had come from the neighbouring district of British Uganda, had had to return home equally frustrated.

Gevers was very upset and could not really understand what it was all about. He thought there must be a mistake and that apologies would be forthcoming. Meanwhile, turned back to the outskirts of the Park, he had to content himself with gazing across six miles at a cone of smoke by day, of fire by night, all the time dreaming of an eruption that would have the decency to choose a terrain outside the jurisdiction of Monsieur le Conservateur. But did the rules and regulations of the Parks permit such scapegrace phenomena?

As for myself, after dropping in briefly at the de Muncks' house, I went back with them to camp once again, and there we stayed for several days, going round the volcano at the respectful distance of two hundred yards and more.

The volcano had taken advantage of our absence to pass from the acute stage of its first period of activity into one which was much more moderate, but quite enough to keep one from approaching too boldly. By this time it was only in exceptional cases the crimson jets of liquid lava rose as high as five hundred feet. Most of the time these 'fountains' dropped back after rising to approximately three hundred feet.

The crater was not, as one might have expected, at the centre of a regular truncated cone, but between two enormous mounds, one of which, slightly higher than the other, culminated in a sort of spur jutting out almost right over the cauldron in which the lava was seething and raging. These two mounds, now about two hundred feet in height, had piled up on the rim of the orifice, being formed by the gushes of magma and gases. In contrast, across the fracture itself hitherto nothing had formed but a slight heaping up of scoriae, and when one stood in the axis of the fissure, one had a view not only of the high fountains of lava and the jets of projectiles rising beyond the limits of the two embankments, but also of the terrific surging of the molten minerals.

BIRD'S EYE VIEW

At that period I twice had the opportunity to fly over the volcano in an aircraft. This enabled me to get an idea of the general appearance of the whole phenomenon and to take a first glance into the raging crater.

The eruption had in fact shot up, as I had supposed, towards the two extremities of an important fracture, which could be clearly seen from the air, gashing the bush for several miles. But the most startling sight was that of the lava that filled the crater, which was white-hot—literally almost white from the intensity of the heat.

On the second flight we saw some pretty impressive rivers of fire, welling up out of fissures that had opened in the base of the cone, and flowing away in blazing torrents.

In spite of the extraordinary nature of it all, I can't

really say that I have kept a very vivid impression of these sights. The very ease with which such an approach is made prevents one from thinking and feeling at all deeply, and leaves one with no clearer a memory than that of an extremely beautiful vision—an image to which one remains more or less a stranger.

Everything that could be seen from the aeroplane—the tongues of fire licking out of the volcano, the boiling inside the vast crater—all this, compared to the glimpses we had had from below, at the cost of innumerable hardships and a certain amount of danger, was of no more real value than Alpine scenery seen from a motor-car, compared to what it means to the mountaineer who has conquered it and made it his own, stone by stone. All the same, this flight over the volcano did enable us to see that the flows issuing from the two centres of activity did not touch each other, there being a space of several miles of forest and savannah between them. We also got a very clear picture of the straight line of the great fracture, a long avenue, denuded of trees, connecting the two focal points of volcanic activity—that in the east, already familiar to us, and that in the west, which had twice driven us back on our attempts to get a foothold there. This western centre was marked out only by several small cones, some of which seemed inactive, while explosions—a little ridiculous from an altitude of three hundred feet—sent the firebrands flying out of certain others.

The two main flows of lava, each issuing from one of the volcanoes, crawled through the dark-green bush like immense black centipedes. The first had not passed the point where it had stopped after a week's progress, when we had gone round it in order to escape being encircled.

A MIRACULOUS FISHING EXPEDITION

The second flow, which was about a mile and a quarter wide, had reached the shores of Lake Kivu and gone on for several hundred yards along the bottom of the lake

itself. From the aeroplane we could distinctly see its outlines through the clear water.

The moment it entered the lake, a thick column of
steam went whirling up to a very great altitude. I was
then at Goma with my friends. We at once returned to
Buheno and, jumping into the motor-boat, dashed off to
see the phenomenon at close quarters.

Suddenly turned into steam, the water was shooting up
in roaring jets which rose at great speed and then united
and mingled, forming a sort of mighty moving pillar that
was constantly bursting into bud, proliferating in rolls and
beads and white udder-like shapes rising towards the
ceiling of grey cloud. The wide front of the lava flow
had already congealed, and the magma, which went on
appearing, had to blaze trails for itself, through the inter-
stices and breaks in the solidified shell. As soon as one of
these red tongues touched the surface of the water, a fresh
jet shot up, whistling with fury, and became part of the
tower of steam that loomed high over the whole scene.

We were more than a hundred fathoms from the edge
of it. Someone dipped his hand into the water. It was
very hot. The thermometer showed eighty degrees centigrade.

'I think we'd better take to the oars,' Adrien said. It
was certainly no use trying to cool the little engine by
using water as hot as this.

We pursued our course, doing some pretty haphazard
oarsmanship, but warily, since every minute we expected
to be driven back by the heat. Far from it. Rowing on,
much to our astonishment, we came into the immediate
neighbourhood of the incandescent tongues and the jets
of steam whose whistling was agony to the ears. We had
one surprise after another: right up against the lava flow,
the temperature of the water was no more than twenty
degrees . . .

On reflection, the thing was easy enough to explain.
The marked differences in temperature caused by the
ebullition of drops of water in direct contact with the

molten torrent had set strong currents moving all over the bay, and this churning process sent the boiling water out into the middle of the lake and let water at a normal temperature flow in to take its place.

'It only needs some nerve and you could take a dip right alongside the red-hot lava,' Adrien commented. 'And to think you'd be boiled alive two hundred fathoms away!'

However, nobody took it upon himself to risk diving in.

At times passing through wisps of hot mist, we rowed along the front of the flow, keeping several fathoms clear of it; it was a hostile succession of black capes and creeks surrounded by rugged basalt. In places eddies more violent than usual disturbed the water on which we were floating, and big bubbles came bursting up to the surface. This was the gases escaping from some tongue of magma seeping under the solidified shell and still crawling slowly along the floor of the lake. These sudden puffs brought us whiffs of the now familiar smell of sulphur. Then Adrien leaned overboard and with one hand scooped up a telapia about six inches long: the fish went on wriggling faintly, now and then flicking its tail against the bottom of the boat, where it had been dropped.

We soon noticed quantities of fish floating on the water, belly upwards. Some of them were partly boiled, particularly the smallest. The more vigorous larger fish must mostly have made their escape to cooler regions.

Doubtless previous eruptions had made the natives familiar with this phenomenon, for at this very moment we saw the dug-out canoes arriving. They came from every point along the bay, each slender craft with a man wielding a paddle fore and aft. The miraculous haul of fish was to last for several weeks.

BAPTISING KITURO

'This volcano has got to be given a name,' I said to myself one day.

And I called one of the native porters who was rather brighter than his comrades.

'Hi, Voiture! What do you call that fire-mountain?'

'Singiro, Bwana.'

Singiro, in the local dialect, means 'volcano'. Logical, of course . . . but perhaps not quite satisfactory for our slightly more complicated white men's minds.

'Well, Voiture, what do you call that place there, that part of the bush?'

I knew that the bush, which to a white man seems exactly the same in one place as in another, seems much more varied to the eyes of the natives. This thick jungle, in normal times inhabited by some scattered pygmies, and traversed by hunters and those in search of wild honey, is not anonymous. There are plenty of names for various parts of it. The natives' minds distinguish countless subtle differences and find a name for each locality.

'Here, no name,' the man replied, jabbing his forefinger in the direction of the ground.

He must have thought I was asking for the name of the bank I was sitting on.

'No, no, not here. There, on the volcano!'

'There, no name.'

Discouraging, this . . .

'But *there*,' he went on, pointing to the rain-water pool some hundred yards behind him, round which the porters had built their wattle hut, 'there, Kineza.'

A name at last! But now Voiture was off.

'And *there*, Kituro.'

He pointed to a spot some hundreds of yards to the north-east of the volcano, much nearer to the crater than the pool was.

'And there, Nyefunzi.'

This time it was at a slightly greater distance to the south.

'And over there,' he said, waving his hand at the great flow of black basalt that was still steaming quietly, 'far away over there, before excrements of God, there was pool of water. Novovo ya Biti. And there . . .'

'Stop, stop, Voiture! That's enough!'

I had far too great a range to choose from.

Although I would have preferred Kineza, as being easier to pronounce, I decided on Kituro, the name of the place closest to the volcano.

'Didkina ya kilima ya moto ni Kituro,' I therefore proclaimed.

Thus was the baptism celebrated.

CHAPTER VII

TOWARDS THE WESTERN VOLCANO

KITURO having been baptised, it was only proper that a name should also be found for its twin brother, that western vent that I had first tried to get to and which had proved itself so forbidding. But how was one to name something one hadn't yet seen face to face? It became evident that a new expedition must be made in that direction.

Fortunately the flight over the area had clarified my ideas about local topography, and I now envisaged a route to the western vent which would go round to the north of Kituro, join up with the great fracture and then follow the line of it towards the west. This approach, if it turned out to be practicable, would have the additional advantage of enabling me to make a complete exploration of the fracture itself.

Taking along with me my faithful Paya and Kaniepala, my excellent though tough-looking cook-boy, I began by skirting the fresh lava that stretched out under the northern slope of the volcano. The ten days' paroxysm had scarred the bush and laid a thick blanket of lapilli over the tree-trunks and stumps which would otherwise have been obstacles in our way. On this side the flow of lava had not, as elsewhere, flung out those chaotic heaps of something resembling clinkers or dumps of coke, but had spread out, forming surfaces that were relatively solid, although only very rarely smooth.

With its waves, billows, and ripples of gloomy rock, it all looked rather like a sea, with a heavy swell on, that had suddenly turned to stone. There were vast areas of flat slabs, more or less streaked with cracks; and in other places there were long, narrow avenues, the surface of which at a closer approach resembled thick coils of rope or cables drawn tightly together. On the edge of these flows, lying on a slab of smooth lava, we came upon the body of a dainty little antelope, quite shrivelled up and by this time badly hacked about by the birds of prey.

We then struck off on to a fairly clearly marked track leading across a grassy savannah, but I soon decided to leave this in order to steer straight south, and it was not long before we came out, as I had hoped, upon the big fracture. Here, I found, it gaped pretty wide. Its still swollen lips bore witness to the colossal pressure of the gases that had opened it up. Here and there the trees in the savannah had been torn up by the roots. Scoriae and blocks of various shapes and sizes were scattered all over the ground round about.

Leaning over the narrow gulf, I tried in vain to plumb its depth. The sunlight lit up the first few feet, revealing layer upon layer of stratified lava that had piled up there in the course of the centuries: some were blackish, others had been stained by rain or by long-vanished volcanic vapours, which had dyed them in bright colours—yellow, red, or in some places almost white. But deeper down everything soon vanished into utter blackness. Out of the gloomy depths there rose only the evanescent smell of carbonic oxide.

I got out of Paya's rucksack fifty yards of rope which I had brought with me, being, after all, an old Alpine mountaineer, on the off-chance that it might come in handy. I tied a biggish stone to one end of it and let the rope run through my fingers . . . The whole length paid out without meeting any obstacle. We hauled this home-made

plumb-line in again and added a good thirty yards of
string, which the far-sighted Paya always carried with
him. Eighty yards were plumbed in this way without our
hitting the bottom or touching any sort of ledge. Puffs
of acrid gas blew out of the abyss now and then, as though
to warn us against rash impulses to go down ourselves.
And yet there was something dreadfully attractive about
those enigmatic depths!

It was possible that at a hundred, or say at two hundred,
fathoms the masses of screes that had fallen in, or the
upper layer of the congealed magma were masking the
bottom of this strange pit. But it might equally well be
that the whole thing went down to far more amazing
depths. . . . The stones that we dropped in—taking care
to let them fall dead in the centre—went hurtling down
with a faint whistling sound. Tense, straining our ears
there above the abyss, we counted the seconds: twenty,
twenty-one, twenty-two . . . the whistling faded, and
then there was silence. We went on listening, hoping to
catch the sound of the bump as the stone reached the
bottom. Nothing . . . One after the other, the rocks we
dropped down vanished into impenetrable depths of
silence.

I decided to sacrifice an old electric torch in the cause
of curiosity. After padding it with several thicknesses of
paper and handkerchiefs tied round it with string, and
stretching a network of protective string across the glass,
I switched it on. With the greatest of care the device was
launched into the abyss.

Almost at once the lighted lens became no more than
a glow-worm, alternatively lighting up and going out, as
the torch whirled round on its way down, and then it was
a mere spark, growing fainter and fainter, further and
further away.

'Thirty-four, thirty-five, thirty-six!'

The luminous dot became minute, infinitesimal. Then
we no longer saw anything.

We moved on.

On two later occasions I made a detour to return to the fracture. It looked the same each time. In one place, however, a short tongue of lava had come licking out and then had congealed, and, a little further on, the walls of the great trench had crumbled in, blocking it up.

Four hours' walking brought us to the edge of a wide field of pillow lava, more or less the same as the one we had come across on the northern side of Kituro. A hundred paces further on we discovered a cone fifty or sixty feet in height from which a sort of belching was emitted at intervals, each time followed by a burst of red magma spreading out fanwise into the air. The burst fell back in a pasty condition, and we could hear the sound of big lumps of it thudding on the steep sides of the cone.

We still lacked the experience that would have enabled us to know for sure which was solid ground and which was not, so we ventured on to the lava only step by step, gingerly putting a foot down on a point chosen by eye, and then delicately transferring one's weight to it. I was not at all keen on breaking through the crust and having my leg—if not more—sink into the burning magma! This cautious progress was strangely like crossing a glacier on which fresh-fallen snow hides the crevasses from the mountaineer's eye. In time I became experienced and learnt to make my way with the greatest of ease over the surface of lava that had been moving only a quarter of an hour before. As a general rule all one needs to do is to move fast and very lightly, on the ball of the foot or, even better, on the toes, wearing rope-soled canvas sneakers or supple shoes with rubber soles. But that day, being still a novice and over-much impressed by the thought of the fragility of those glassy slabs beneath which I imagined layer upon layer of soft, burning stuff, I preferred to beat a retreat to the edge.

It was none too easy to follow the fringe of the forest, since it was strewn with trees of all sizes that had been sapped at the base by the hot, flowing lava. The chaotic entanglements of branches reminded us of our agonising adventure a fortnight previously. We got round it by taking a short cut across the lava flow. After some time, the nature of these flows changed, the smooth 'pillow' lava giving place to alarming-looking embankments of slag formed by scoriaecous lava. It took us an hour and twenty minutes to cover about two hundred yards, after which a clearing in the forest and a little hillock gave us a chance, at last, to get a general glimpse of this centre of volcanic activity.

In the middle of a field of lava that seemed to be more or less circular, a chain of little knolls stretched out for more than two hundred yards. It was obvious that these hillocks —which are called *spatter-cones*—jutted up out of the great fracture. Some of them were sporadically emitting jets of molten lava; others seemed extinct. Smoke and steam came out of numerous places on the surface of the lava flow, preventing us from getting a detailed picture of this queer landscape. It was indeed a strange sight, under the dark, glowering sky, in that vast silence, punctuated now and then by the sound of an explosion as something 'went off', and the patter of a descending shower of pasty magma. Here was a grey, chaotic plain over which innumerable whitish clouds of steam, all drifting parallel in the wind, looked like supernatural gauze veils, and all around the edges stood the sombre encircling guard of great dead trees.

Behind us was a steep slope covered with very dense vegetation. This was Mount Shové, that ancient cinder-cone whose base, hidden in the forest, we had probably gone round that day when we had had to run from the molten lava.

We climbed up this hill and pitched our tent on its summit, under an immense wild fig-tree. I have rarely seen a more wonderful tree-trunk. Smooth, pale grey in colour, it was six or seven yards round the base and rose, narrowing, towards the magnificent spread of its gigantic branches. The trunk was not even, but deeply grooved, with ridges rising out of the dark slots, rather like woody flying-buttresses the whole way round the tree. This fig-tree is famous throughout the district, for it can be clearly seen for nearly twenty miles around.

ADVENTURES BY NIGHT

Darkness fell swiftly, and the glow of the lava was once again reflected from the low clouds. Climbing up into the lowest branches of the fig-tree, we squatted there, the two Negroes and myself, gazing at this immense nocturnal world into which the volcanoes flung out their crimson glare. From here, at a single glance, we could see the whole gigantic chain of volcanoes, stretching from huge Nira-gongo, some fifteen miles away, to the incandescent vents seething at the very foot of our observatory. All that could be made out of Niragongo was the mighty plume of smoke, gleaming red. Nearer to us was Kituro, its ceaseless throb-bing flinging fiery bursts towards the sky, its fumes a whirling crimson darkness. Round its base the lava flows sprinkled the night with streaks and dots of light. Quite near us red jaws gaped open, and strings of scarlet specks marked the outflows now partly blanketed in cold lava.

Leaving Kaniepala to guard the tent and taking Paya along with me, I left the camp to go down the other side of the hill and try to discover the cause of the more intense illumination reflected by the clouds in that direction.

Armed with a machete and an electric torch, we followed a wide track which the elephants had opened among those enormous gramini that bear their name—elephant-grass. From time to time the machete had to go into action to overcome some obstacle that the pachyderms had not bothered to trample down. All in all, however, we made easy progress.

Suddenly a sort of faint whistling brought us up short. It stopped, even as we stood straining our ears, and then began again. We had no difficulty in placing it on our left, about a pace away. I switched on the electric torch. In its light there was revealed a little hollow formed of creepers, grasses and brambles. After some thirty seconds the hissing became fainter and stopped. There was a brief lull, and then again there it was, faintly hoarse: it was as though gases under only slight pressure were being set free at regular intervals through a fairly large orifice.

Under the narrow beam from the torch I rummaged about among this tangle of greenery with the machete, trying to find some crack in the ground. Could this be the prelude to a re-awakening of the old cinder-cone of Shové? Or was it caused by gases from the active area alongside, which, for heaven knows what reasons, had drilled out a path for themselves through the bulk of this extinct cinder-cone, to escape near its summit?

The sound began again, inexplicable, slightly disturbing . . .

I suddenly got an idea. I stopped tapping at the thicket with the machete, switched off the torch, straightened up and looked at Paya.

'Iko sawa-sawa nyama?' ('Do you think it's an animal?') I asked in a low voice.

'Ndio, Bwana. Chui,' my companion whispered ('Yes, Master, leopard.').

I switched the light on again, but could not make out anything but the intertwinings of twigs and grasses, out of which the whistling, snoring sound issued once again.

With our eyes fixed on this disquieting thicket, we began to walk backwards, quietly, oh, very quietly indeed . . . One step, another step, and another . . . and another . . . At last, suddenly taking to our heels, we fled for all we were worth!

I shall never know which of us was more frightened—the leopard or ourselves. For there was not much doubt about it, it was a leopard all right. Going back there the next day, we found the fresh paw-marks which it had left, and recent droppings, whitish, containing tufts of hair from the animal's last feed. He must have had some startling sensations, similar to our own, when he had the beam of an electric torch flashed straight into his eyes. Fortunately the wind was blowing in our direction and he cannot have picked up our scent.

Running on through the darkness, we reached the extremity of the long ridge crowning the horseshoe of Mount Shové. There, through the big trees covering the slope, there, right at our feet, sparkled the source of light that we were in search of. . . . We climbed down as fast as we could, our hands stretched out in front of us, slipping from one tree-trunk to the next. Suddenly we were out of the forest. Ahead of us, barely a hundred yards away, flowed a fairy-tale river. . . .

Intense yellow and dazzling red, the torrent—of some apparently turgescent substance—poured along in strange silence, a huge line of light cutting across the black background of the basalt. On its surface, filigreed with moving arabesques, was the delicate thin skin that forms as lava cools.

We stood motionless and speechless, startled by a sight of such overwhelming beauty.

After a long time a murmur issued from Paya's lips:

'Lualaba ya moto, Lualaba ya moto . . .' ('Lualaba of fire, Lualaba of fire . . .')[1]

Yes, that was about it. That latent force, that silent swiftness, were the force and swiftness of a river—a river of fire.

I pulled myself together and tried to estimate some measurements. Width—it must be about thirty feet across, or perhaps a little less. It seemed to issue from a tunnel. Blazing golden-yellow at its source, it gradually changed into a wonderful orange colour, which in turn became vermilion, then scarlet, at which stage the fine translucid skin began to form on its surface. The flux swept it along at about twelve miles an hour. The skin darkened, stretched, was punctuated by holes that were at first round and then, as they were swiftly drawn out, became elliptical; it was like dough becoming distended to breaking-point, some-

---

[1] Lualaba is the name given to the upper reaches of the Congo River. Paya came from the Lualaba region.

times tapering off to a very thin line. The speed was so great that the surface film could not quite manage to cover the incandescent magma, and these arabesques of stretched or broken rings were the only flecks of black.

At a guess, I put the length of the river at something over half a mile. Beyond that the red changed very rapidly into very dark purple, and the fresh lava soon disappeared under a solid black shell.

I wanted to get closer to this extraordinary avalanche. Dazzled by the blaze of it, I advanced rather clumsily, sliding down the bank of scoriae and stumbling into the heaped blocks and brittle slabs. But a sensation of panic arose within me, growing stronger, telling me it was impossible to cross this chaos of lava: supposing I were suddenly to go through the crust and plunge into the burning magma? Regretfully, I retreated and went back to join Paya.

We spent hours there watching the fire pouring away into the darkness.

MUHUBOLI

I had baptised this western vent Muhuboli, again on the principle of choosing the name of the nearest locality. With experience behind me, I was no longer afraid to walk over the fields of lava. Unfortunately I had no further chance to see a river of fire so splendid, so rapid, and so long.

Muhuboli, as it appeared to us the first time we saw it, consisted of a series of spatter-cones, some only seven or eight feet high, the others rising to forty-five feet or so. They were formed, for the most part, by the agglomeration of clots of magma which had fallen in a pasty state, having been flung out of the vent at the centre of each cone. I often leaned over one of those fathomless black mouths, lying flat on my belly on the steep side of the cone, my face exposed to the sulphurous exhalations rising from the depths. Each time I longed for a day when I should have at my disposal all the necessary equipment—asbestos suit, mask, breathing-apparatus, windlass and cable—and have myself let right down as far as I could go into one of these abysses, down towards the inconceivable unknown interior of the earth.

The great fracture still yawned fairly wide open at various points on Muhuboli and in places we could see it nibbling at the lower slopes of the cones. Between some of these cones there was a series of pools of lava, now solidified, cutting across the fissure. This volcano, Muhuboli, thus presented a curious example of the segregation of gases and lava, the former being driven out only through the conduits ending in the spatter-cones, the latter being emitted by the vents interspersed between these spatter-cones. The gases, it seemed, generally escape at higher levels than the lava. This was exemplified in the present eruption, taken as a whole: the explosive centre, where the gases gushed out in great quantities and with great virulence, was localised on Kituro, at an altitude of approximately 5,900 feet, whereas the almost exclusively lava-producing centre of Muhuboli, situated at the western extremity of the same fissure, was no more than about 5,250 feet high. However, in the case of Muhuboli itself this rule was not confirmed, for although the gases—which were emitted, incidentally, only in relatively slight quantities—were distinctly separated from the liquid outflow, they did not escape by way of the highest points but followed channels *alternating* with those through which the magma was evacuated.

In the course of the explorations that I later made on and around Muhuboli, I found the explanation for the gush of lava, so sudden and unexpected after several days of intense activity, which had so aggressively cut off our retreat with the truck. Between the two cinder-cones, Shové and Rumoka, both of which stood about a thousand feet high in a plain of basalt, a vast and more or less circular depression had been hollowed out, a sort of immense dish, about three miles wide and ten or fifteen feet deep. The lava that had been so abundantly emitted by Muhuboli from the first day of its eruption[1] accumulated in this depression, and during the next few days gradually rose to the brim. Millions of cubic feet of magma piled up in this way and then, when the dish was full, suddenly overflowed, and went pouring down towards Lake Kivu. It reached the lake in less than forty hours, covering an area about five miles long and two wide. This was the inopportune flooding which had so very nearly trapped us, leaving us only just time to run for it. It will be remembered that we had had to abandon the truck with all our heavy equipment. Returning that same day, however, we had been able—thanks to an old track that we discovered in the bush—to drive the precious vehicle down to the shore of the lake, and soon afterwards have it taken off by a barge.

[1] *See Appendix* I (c).

CHAPTER VIII

THE WITCHES' BREW

. . . il focó eterno Ch'entro l'afóca, le dimostra rosse.
(The eternal fire that heats them from within makes them red to
look upon.)

Dante, *Inferno* VIII, 73, 74

DURING the six weeks the eruption had been going
on I had never dared to venture into the chaos of solidified
lava round the very foot of Kituro.

Looking not unlike a slag-heap, this brand-new volcano
towered over black surroundings where there was nothing
familiar, nothing of known proportions, to provide one
with a scale of measurement. It might just as easily have
been a thousand feet high as a hundred or two, and it
might have been more than half a mile away, or only two
hundred paces. A rough triangulation, the only kind
possible in that jungle, had informed me that the volcano
must be between 150 and 250 feet in height and that the
camp was about a quarter of a mile away from it.

That day, 14 April, having once again patrolled all
round the limit of the outflows, I was returning to camp,
feeling very empty in the stomach after my usual daily
foot-slog of several hours.

I had stopped at the point, right in the axis of the
fissure, from where one could see the molten magma
seething between the two embankments of the cone.

I noticed some kites wheeling over the smoke and fumes. Now, what on earth could be attracting them to such a place, where there was no prey, where no living thing could survive? Doubtless they were mistaking the eruption for one of those bush-fires that give them easy pickings, with the chance to drop down on panic-stricken rabbits and other small rodents.

But must not this mean that there was some way of getting a little closer to this prodigious phenomenon? I felt the black surface of the outflow with my hand: it was luke-warm, although at the bottom of the cracks I could just glimpse an only gradually darkening gleam of crimson.

I hauled myself up and then made my way ahead cautiously. The ground held. . . . Since nothing was coming down on my head, I advanced faster, counting my strides in order to get an idea of the distance I was covering.

After two hundred steps I found myself at the foot of the cone. I knew what I wanted to know: a very rough calculation enabled me to deduce that the height of the cone must be about three hundred feet.

Walking on this ground that no human foot had ever stepped on before, where not even a bird had alighted, I had a strange feeling of satisfaction. Was it pride? I don't think so. For what reason, after all, was there for pride? Had I encountered the least difficulty? It was rather more the awareness of an exceptional stroke of luck and an exceptional privilege.

This subtle intoxication did not prevent my glancing up at the sky. It was not to thank the heavens or implore their aid, but simply to avoid being bumped into by one of the large projectiles that I occasionally saw crumbling away from the steep sides of the cone. Satisfied, I was about to turn and go on back to camp, when I was struck by an idea: since I had managed to get this far, why shouldn't I push on to the summit and try to have a glance into the crater itself? To reach the lip of a crater *in eruption* was well worth a risk.

What was rather queer was that the rumblings from the volcano were not as loud here as some distance away. This was undoubtedly because sound is not so easily conducted through a rocky wall as through air. This relative peacefulness gave me a certain amount of confidence, although in another way it made me vaguely feel the presence of a threat.

Being driven back towards the left by exhalations of hot gases, I found a less hostile area and set about scrambling up with all possible speed, often on all fours, through the unsteady heaps of the lava-blocks. But the faster I tried to go the less progress I made; for once the precarious balance of these heaps was disturbed, they had an exasperating tendency to come rolling down and to carry me with them.

After a little of this performance I was quite out of breath. I had already had to give up any hope of watching out for bombs coming down on me. Reassuring myself with a metaphorical pat on the back and an inward mutter of 'Steady now', I gave my mind to the problem of advancing as carefully and cautiously as possible, still, of course, on all fours. Remembering what years of boxing had taught me, and the agony of having no breath left at the end of each round, I forced myself to take long deep breaths through my nose and then to breathe out as completely as I could. Without having to make any further stops, I managed by this means to re-establish a normal breathing-rhythm.

And now, raising my head again, I could at last see the very top of the cone just ahead. At this very instant half a dozen lumps of magma, still pasty, plumped down there. Two of them rolled down the declivity, and I turned for a second to follow the course of one of them, which went past me only two paces to my right.

In another few minutes I was standing upright on the summit, which at this point was about a yard wide. On my left sloped away the scarp up which I had just climbed, and on my right was a sheer drop of some fifty feet into a ravine of black scoriae. This meant there was a wall, or rather an interior cone, still separating me from the true crater. The noise had again grown very loud, now that it was so near. There were muffled, mighty rumblings, punctuated by explosions. Keeping a weather-eye open for the denser falls of projectiles, I started out with long strides. A few seconds later, after prudently stepping over or round a series of yawning cracks, I found myself, much to my surprise, on the very crest of the narrow bluff overlooking the crater.

This crater was about fifty yards long, running east and west, and about thirty-five across. There were thirty feet of steep slope between the high rim and the colossal frothing of crimson matter that kept being flung up in furious waves. Puffs of bluish smoke exhaled from the abyss partially veiled the red of the lava, which lashed without pause against the surrounding walls. The incandescent basalt, which was extraordinarily liquid, would splash up the side of the wall, sometimes even licking the top of it, and then, after a fraction of a second's hesitation, would flow back again at terrifying speed. In the middle of this gigantic cauldron the lava boiled and bubbled, throwing up red foam on a pool of red, a fiery froth upon a lake of fire.

A brief glance behind me showed me the vast panorama of black lava stretching away to distant Lake Kivu, a large twinkling patch of something like grey metal.

During the meal, sitting in the opening of the tent, I told Kaniepala and Paya what I had seen, describing my feelings as well as I could translate them into Swahili. Squatting on their heels, they listened to my story, smiling and wagging their heads.

For them I had already long ceased to be a white man exactly like all other white men. To put it plainly, they evidently thought me mildly crazy. Of course they were no longer unaware why I had this strange habit of collecting stones and hammering till I had splintered them, and why every day I came back to camp loaded down with fragments of such stones, which I had first scrutinised minutely through a 'little glass' and then licked (a geologist's little trick). They knew now that all this sometimes led to the discovery of a gold or tin mine where many Negroes would go and work. But for all that, their first impression from this series of queer actions had never completely disappeared. For some weeks now the fact that I went roaming around the 'devils' mountains' for no apparent reason had been tending to confirm their original opinion of me. But today their *bwana* had actually gone walking around the very edge of the crater! And however incredible it might seem, he had actually returned. And all in one piece. The gods watch over those who are mad.

'One of these days he will jump into the hole to see what is inside. And you may be sure he will come back to dinner as usual and tell us to make three pints of tea because he is very thirsty. Perhaps even more than three pints . . .'

It was twilight, and then the hot night spread swiftly over our world.

I was sitting down outside the tent, once again allowing myself to dream as I gazed at the scarlet fireworks in the sky. Without pause they were flung up, again and again, scattering in showers, and falling in a hail of dramatic volutes. A few paces away the two natives squatted by their little fire, telling each other endless stories, in low voices.

So now I knew what there was inside the crater. Of course, I had known it even before I went there, but that was fundamentally different: now I knew it because I had seen it, I had beheld it with my own eyes. I had had the good luck to see for myself an astonishing and as it were supernatural spectacle, one that left me exhausted now, sitting on the edge of the camp bed, but full of a new feeling of affection for *my* volcano.

CHAPTER IX

A NIGHT AMONG THE FLAMES

OVER the tops of the tall grasses I saw advancing towards me a head, adorned with a felt hat, on a pair of bowed shoulders. Behind this apparition came two other heads, black, and bearing large loads. While the little group came on, following the winding track that had gradually been beaten out by porters bringing up supplies to our camp, I said to myself: Here are some visitors who must have got up with the lark. For there was a journey of several hours to be made through the bush after leaving the motor-road. This lap of the journey did not seem to have tired the white man, who was walking ahead. His lithe, sure-footed progress revealed him, even at that distance, to be someone thoroughly at home in the bush.

Arriving in front of me, he pulled up short, a slender figure in a khaki blouse crossed by the strap of a little knapsack slung behind him. Lifting his grey felt hat with an urbane air that one hardly expected in those solitary wilds, and smiling, he announced in a quiet, rather husky voice:

'My name is Richard—Jacques Richard.'

'How do you do.'

'How do you do. Monsieur and Madame de Munck assured me I would not be too late to see something interesting.'

'Yes, indeed. I hope you're not tired? Then I'll show you at once.'

This was how I came to know the volcanologist Richard.

Actually he was a planter by occupation. But his daring, his intellectual curiosity, and his interest in every aspect and secret of this country, were far too great for him to confine himself to agriculture. He had begun his career in Java, that island of volcanoes. Later, when he set up in Kenya, he had begun successively exploring the volcanic vents in the African continent. The planter earned a living for the volcanologist, but the volcanologist forgot all about the planter at the first news of an eruption. Acting like a powerful magnet on a light steel needle, my Kituro had torn him away from his milking-cows and his pyrethrum plantations.

For several days on end we scouted around the volcano and its surroundings, observing the nature of the lava, taking specimens of the salts deposited by the fumes, noting temperatures, and making chemical experiments on the gases exhalted from the fissures and the vents that riddled all parts of the volcanic area. From the very first I had taken a liking to him, with his thin tanned face. We had a passion in common. No more was needed to bring about a staunch friendship and mutual exchange of confidence.

Our first enterprise, that very first morning, was a visit to the crater. I had got into the habit of going up there every day to see what was going on inside the cauldron. The enthusiasm shown by this stolid, extremely reserved man, who had been visiting volcanoes all over the globe for the past twenty years, made me realise how very exceptional this glimpse right into the crater of a volcano in eruption was even for someone who knew the subject.

He pointed out to me in the course of our fortnight together what very marked variations there were in the explosive activity of Kituro. In periods of relative lull the projectiles hardly rose higher than the edges of the crater, whereas at times when activity was more virulent the bombs hurtled up to something like three hundred feet higher than the summit itself. Such variations are generally attributed to fluctuations in the explosive potential of the volcano; but having observed what was going on right in the crater's mouth at various times while it was active, I had been able to establish that in fact the bursts always rose to a more or less constant height over the surface of the magma, but that this surface itself was subject to considerable and rapid changes of level. One day, for example, the lava would almost fill the crater and the projectiles would rise very high over the rim, whereas the next day the lava might have completely disappeared from sight, leaving that mighty funnel empty for more than a hundred feet down, to where at the bottom one could see the lurid glare of the chimney itself; on such days the bombs never rose to more than two or three times a man's height over the rim of the crater.

On the evening of 3 May we noticed that the level of the lava must have risen, judging by the luminous intensity of the reflections on the plume of smoke and the violence of the explosions. This gave us the feeling that we would like to go up to the summit in the course of the night. A little before the short equatorial twilight we set off down the winding path that I had had hacked out in the bush a short time earlier in order to save me from having to come back all the way round by the great fissure.

After descending into the scrub-covered hollow, which was all that remained of what had formerly been the valley, we got going on outflows of the 'corded lava' type. This sort of lava has a relatively smoothly congealed surface. But here it was so much broken and churned up by flows that had come down after it had solidified that the chaos of enormous blocks and slabs reared up on end—slabs leaning sideways, slabs piled up on each other, and

so forth—had become as ticklish to cross as the kind
of lava known in Hawaii as *aa* and in Auvergne as *cheires*,
which is so frightful to travel across that in the volcanic
regions of the New World it is called *malpais*, 'bad country'.

Our route took us round the worst bits, being clearly
indicated by the trace of fine lapilli that we had crushed
underfoot since we had used that trail. There would be
splendid straight logs of lava ten paces or so in length,
and then suddenly, in order to avoid knife-edged slabs or
unsteady heaps, we would have very carefully to follow
the precise meanderings of the trail, which often described
as many as twelve right-angled bends in a distance of
three yards.

After ten minutes we entered into the area on the
southern circumference of the volcano: this area was completely blanketed in a layer of ash ten or twelve feet deep.
In the middle of this desert of black dunes stood a little
group of trees, reduced to skeletons, their withered branches
reaching up into the air. We stopped for a short rest at
the foot of the cone, waiting for nightfall. A swarm of
huge-winged birds cruised unwearyingly around the crater,
outlined against the glaring sky. The blood-red light gave
a lurid tone to the strange ring they formed around the
cauldron. Then, following the route we now knew well,
we climbed the slopes leading up to the summit. When
we raised our eyes we would sometimes see the orange
burst of an explosion, and sometimes it would happen
that lumps of magma came spattering down on the slopes
above us, where we could see the glow swiftly dying out
of them. Some of these fiery pebbles did not stop but rolled
on down towards the base, in bigger and bigger bounds,
streaking the darkness with scallops of light.

Then we came out on the edge of the crater.

The terrible heat hit us in the face just as the sight of the
great cauldron seething with molten gold pulled us up
short.

Tall fountains of lava were shooting straight up into
the air and spattering a foam of fire all round them as

they fell back again. From time to time a sudden burst of projectiles went hurtling towards the sky. Bubbles, bursting on the surface of the heavy liquid, released great puffs of purple vapour. All this fury was localised in three or four spots on this tremendous lake of liquid rock. The rest surged ponderously under the driving-force of those points of intense virulence, and, hypnotised, we watched this foaming molten matter, which was underlined by a sparkling beam of yellow, beating against the wall on the far side of the crater.

This cliff opposite, about forty yards away, was itself tinged red from the reflection of the intense heat. Under our feet, the cliff on the summit of which we were standing must be equally incandescent: the unbearable heat kept us three or four paces back from the edge.

The necessity to take measurements and other observations aroused us from our bemused state. We had to hold our cameras out at arm's length in order to get them nearer than we could bring our faces, and our hands then came in for a merciless toasting.

We had measured the temperature of the lava by pyroscope: it oscillated around eleven hundred and fifty degrees centigrade, with some measurements exceeding twelve hundred. Where we were at that moment the temperature of the air, vitiated by sulphur and hydrochloric acid fumes, was about seventy degrees, but a yard further on it was more than eighty. It was absolutely impossible, that night, to go right up to the rim and lean over the burning lava, the surface of which was barely twenty feet below the lips of the crater.

We stayed nearly twenty minutes up there. It was so extraordinarily powerful and splendid an experience that we could not get enough of it. The incandescent lava was no longer dimmed by competition with daylight, and its terrible radiance, striking straight through the purple smoke, was the only thing one could think of here in the darkness of the night.

However, our feet were beginning to feel the effects of

standing on that hot ground, and the rumbling of bombs and lapilli showering down round us grew menacing. The instinct of self-preservation had been urging us to run away from the very beginning and now we gave way to it. Every second strained our nerves still more, and the intoxicated ecstasy we felt at the beauty of it was closely bound up with the panic we had been suppressing.

Buckling our packs, we turned our backs on that great cooking-pot, which would doubtless have been greatly to the taste of the witches in *Macbeth*, and scrambled down the outer slope. Half-way down, both tripping at the same instant, we found ourselves flat on our faces side by side. And there we lay, relaxed, hilarious, while we saw, with a wild joy and a vague sense of retrospective terror, a terrific cone of fire shoot up and come hailing down in a dense shower on the very spot where we had been standing a minute earlier.

CHAPTER X

NYAMLAGIRA

Buheno, 5 May

THE VOLCANIC world is a sombre one: grey, dark blue, brown fading into black. The rare notes of light colour are yellow, white or ochre, which mark the saline deposits left by the fumes, and they only succeed in making the general scene appear more gloomy than ever. As for the dark or dazzling reds and golds of molten lava, the exaltation they arouse is every time followed by a vague depression. Twenty-four hours spent in such surroundings cause only enthusiasm, but after the third or fourth day the human animal gradually falls a prey to uneasiness. One longs to see water . . . plants . . .

We had a real sense of relief in the moment when we turned our backs on the volcano to resume our journey through the savannah. Even the coloured porters, who actually hardly ever went beyond the relatively safe precincts of the camp itself, were cheered from that instant and were noisily laughing and chattering. True, volcano or no volcano, the natives are always delighted to be going home again: the sweet prospect of returning to wife or wives, to *pombé*, that thick beer of theirs, the *batotos* (the children) and their *ndukus* (friends), was quite enough to elevate them into this state of jollity.

As ever, Buheno is a real little paradise. The green of

the lawns and the blue of the lake are enchanting, and even more so, perhaps, the bright colours of the flowers.

6 May, evening

Natives coming in from the bush tell stories of explosions bursting out at the foot of Nyamlagira and of how the forest is on fire. Herds of elephants are in flight, they say, and that is a sign of impending catastrophe.

Standing in the doorway, without even the aid of the binoculars we could indeed see fires in the direction they indicated—not very tremendous fires, it seemed, but still, quite numerous. There were thirty or more dots of light, which the binoculars showed to be flames, shooting up along a long straight line. Nevertheless, however we strained our ears, we could not hear anything but the distant roar of Kituro. There was not the slightest sound of explosions, nor anything like whistling. Pending further developments, it did not seem that this phenomenon was of the paroxysmal pattern.

Whatever it might be, Richard and I have decided to set out tomorrow for the Nyamlagira region. We shall sleep in the shelter not far from the summit, and then we shall visit the extinct crater. After that we shall go down the other side and through the forest to reach this new active zone.

7 May, Nyamlagira Observatory

Started at 10.20 a.m., arrived at 3 p.m., drenched.

Made the ascent by a very good path, good because it has been used so much: till 1938 the volcano was very active and visitors were numerous. A cylindrical cinder-cone with vertical sides, about two hundred yards in diameter, of varying depth, then pierced the floor of the vast crater in which a lake of lava was seething. Strictly speaking we are here dealing not with a *crater* at all, i.e. with a large cup at the bottom of which there is a supply channel, but with a *sink-hole*.[1]

[1] *See* Appendix I (d).

From the big wooden hut where we are staying, two hundred yards from the summit, we cannot yet make out anything. This observatory was built for the volcanologist, Jean Verhoogen, who was sent here in 1938 at the time of the great eruption.

This eruption began strangely. Colonel Hoier, who was then in charge of the National Park, saw it happen. After tourists and experts had for years been attesting, by their observations, the permanence of the boiling lake, in 1938 the live lava suddenly disappeared, as though after ages of constant activity the volcano were now becoming dormant. But some days later, according to Colonel Hoier, earthquake tremors accompanied by terrible roars shook the volcanic mountain to its base. Two colossal networks of crevasses opened up in the sides of the cone, one on the south, the other on the east, and torrents of extremely fluid lava gushed forth and poured down on every side. In the *caldera* itself there was a great deal of caving-in of walls, and the appearance of the cinder-cone was soon considerably altered. The eruption was to rage on for almost two years.

Since that time Nyamlagira has returned to a state of lull. Is this now coming to an end?

Saturday, 8 *May*

Excellent night in the old observatory. This morning, starting out before six, we had no trouble in reaching the immense *caldera*, the floor of which, surrounded by steep circular walls from one hundred and fifty to three hundred feet in height, is at an altitude of nearly ten thousand feet. These surrounding walls become steadily lower towards the south-west and there for a certain distance cease altogether. This breach enabled us to get through into the sink-hole without the least difficulty.

The largest part of the bottom of the cauldron, the surface of which is rather more than a square mile in area, is made up of semi-horizontal strata of smooth black lava, while to the south an area where there has been some collapse gives one a view of an immense chaos of rocks and boulders. White fumes and vapour, largely made up of steam and sulphurous gas, escape quietly through little fissures.

It may be more dangerous than one would think to go wandering about on these lovely smooth slabs: it sometimes happens that the magma underneath them withdraws as the surface solidifies, leaving an empty space ten or twenty feet deep. There is nothing on the surface to indicate that if one sets foot on these slabs they may splinter like glass. I once had the bad luck to have this happen to me, but fortunately the hole was not deep and I hauled myself out with only some cuts on one leg. After that we were wiser and more cautious.

Towards the western end we found two large pits, which seemed to me to be over three hundred yards wide and about six hundred feet deep. At the bottom were heaps of stones that had crumbled in, and the surrounding walls were cut off absolutely vertically, which made the structure of the volcano clearly visible: it was composed of an enormous accumulation of lava, layers of lapilli and bombs that had more or less consolidated into *volcanic tuff*.[1]

We went right across the cauldron, reaching the foot of the eastern wall. White fumeroles, which were very active, were escaping through a good many fissures at this point. In the sunshine, of which we were lucky enough to have more than usual today, these immaculate volutes were quite lovely to watch. But what were even more splendid were the deposits of natural sulphur, which was the most beautiful yellow.

This intense vapour-activity is localised to the neighbourhood of the enormous fracture that opened in the side of the volcano in 1938. In order to see it better, we had to go back to the 'entry' to the cauldron and then

[1] In the same way as sink-holes, but on a smaller scale, such pits are caused by the collapse in a solid mass of a whole cylindrical part of the structure. Their mode of formation—this accumulation of strata of hard rock, caused by outflows of lava and crumbly rock from material ejected—has caused volcanoes of this type to be given the name of *cumulo-volcanoes*.

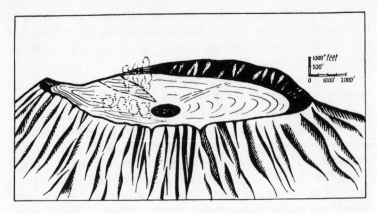

follow the higher rim of the wall round it for nearly two miles. The fracture, which is a good forty yards across, is choked with large blocks that have broken loose and crashed into it. From where we stood at the opening, it vanished from sight further down the slope. There is another on the southern slope, which we shall explore tomorrow.[1]

In the afternoon, the weather, which up to now has been beautiful, suddenly changes. Rain . . . At our feet there stretches away the vast plain formed by the lava emitted by the Virunga volcanoes for thousands of years: eighty square miles, for the most part overgrown now by savannah and jungle, only the very latest outflows cutting their grey lines through the dark green. In the far distance are two bright spots: Lake Kivu and Saké Bay. In the

[1] These fractures are most probably the result of a powerful thrust from below by the magma that is steadily rising through the volcanic structure. Giving way under this pressure, the cone split, following two directions of generative force at right angles to each other, and the lava poured out through these openings. After the short introductory phase, the activity was localised to the lower part of the other fissure, that on the southern side of the mountain, which runs down to a lower level than this one. At the spot called Tchambene, lava and gases went on pouring out for months on end, draining the subterranean reservoir, while no other manifestation of any kind, apart from vapour, was produced at the higher level. It is worth commenting on the fact that the proportion of gases in relation to lava did not exceed 1 per cent, whereas in the Kituro eruption it seems to have been in the region of 30 per cent.

middle of this panorama, which is almost two thousand feet below us, the smoking cone of Kituro seems quite minute. But what interests us is the bluish vapours rising, here and there, from the bush not far from the extinct cinder-cone of Rugwété. Is this all there will be of the heralded catastrophe? There are no other signs that can possibly have anything to do with the alarming news that made us leave Buheno. We shall see tomorrow what it is all about.

Following the edge of the southern fracture, we come down to a level of about 8,400 feet. Then we put up our tent on the very place where Verhoogen pitched camp ten years ago.

Night has fallen. We can see some flames on the plain, but there doesn't seem to be any tendency for the bush to start burning over any wide area.

Sunday, 9 *May*

Following along the fissure, we come out on a pit that I don't remember having found mentioned in Verhoogen's descriptions. Although on a smaller scale, this shaft is of the same type as those we saw in the cauldron yesterday: a huge cylindrical hole that looks as if it had been stamped out by machinery. But here there is a profusion of marvellous yellow sulphur stalactites, a shower of motionless gold dripping from every irregularity in the vertical wall, delighting our eyes in spite of the leaden atmosphere of this damp day.

A little higher up, the lips of the fracture are carpeted with a 'skin' of congealed lava, not more than an inch thick, and looking like a wave of the sea which has surged up with great force and been instantly petrified. The resemblance is so marked that there can be no doubt about it; this is where a violent flood of lava, fluid because it was at such high temperature, burst out of the fissure and trickled in a shallow wave out over its lips.

A long walk through the wonderful forest of giant heather brings us to the outflow that issued from the eastern fracture. Queer shapes have been formed by the lava, things like stone trees, hollow inside. What evidently happened was that in its first early rush the wave of fire literally raced up the trunks of the trees standing along the edges and then fell back after having coated or glazed them. Later the charred wood disappeared, leaving only the moulds to show what had happened. There is another possible explanation, namely that the whole of the first wave was very much higher and that the level of the outflow immediately fell very considerably. Richard and I could not make up our minds which of these two hypotheses was right. We observed that the side of these moulds facing uphill is relatively smooth, while there are appendices fringing the side that faces downhill—which gives one an excellent picture of the direction of the flow.

Richard was walking a pace ahead of me.

Light and sure-footed, he steered deftly along the tortuous track beaten out by wild animals. I enjoyed teaming up with him, all the more because I had often made trips with people who got on my nerves within half a day of starting out.

Richard, on the other hand, was strikingly well-balanced, considerate and tactful, besides having a skill and physical endurance that made it possible to carry out all our plans.

We had been advancing for some time over these chaotic surfaces, which are characteristic of *malpais*, the sharp angles of the scoriae being hardly softened at all by the dense vegetation, in spite of the amount of time that had passed, when suddenly we felt a shock go right through our bodies. This shock was almost instantly followed by a muffled sound like that of a short, sharp, stifled puff. To me it seemed to come from our right, to Richard from somewhere ahead. We separated, but neither of us could discover anything.

Scarcely had we joined up again when another shock
went through us, from the soles of our feet to our heads,
and the same sound followed at once, this time distinctly
coming from somewhere ahead. About ten minutes later
we came to a clearing in the bush, one of the branches of
the 1938 outflow, a wide avenue of stony blocks already
covered with a carpet of grey lichen. Ten years previously
these stones were rolling along at a temperature of a
thousand degrees . . . Today, they were already overgrown with tiny plants. Later, on Mount Etna, in the hot
climate of Sicily, I was to see outflows already half a century
old which were still totally bald.

After some minutes' walking, skirting the forest, we
came on a circular area denuded of trees, about eight
yards across, scattered with charred wood and bits of
pebble and rock. In the centre, an irregularly shaped
hole, partly choked with pieces of rock that had crumbled
down from its sides, was exhaling gases and lazy bluish
vapour. The stones were still hot to the touch, and the
charred pieces of wood, bits of tree-trunks and torn
branches, were still fresh—still *living*. There was no doubt
about it, we had hit on the place of the explosion which
we had felt a quarter of an hour earlier.

We leaned over the abyss. There was nothing to be
seen—nothing but the blackness of the depths between the
fallen blocks, which were jammed up against each other.
We were struck by the very strange smell of the gases.
It was not a mineral smell. It was an *organic* smell, and
one that I had come across before; I was sure of that. But
however much I racked my brains, I could not identify
it. It was faintly sweet and yet at the same time had
a suggestion of bitter almonds. Yet it was not bitter
almonds.

'Cyanide?' Richard suggested.

He shook his head the moment he had spoken. No, it
was not cyanide either. We were sorry we had not the
equipment necessary for taking specimens of gas. There
was nothing for it but to go on wondering.

The rain began to fall again. Crossing the 1938 outflow, we pushed on westward through very dense bush, over very nasty ground. During the next half-hour there were several more explosions, not far from us. Then suddenly we lit on another treeless space in the centre of which, shooting out through a pile of big boulders, yellow and bluish flames were gently snoring . . .

The irregular walls of the vent were tinged reddish yellow. The pyroscope gave a reading of 970 degrees centigrade. Here, as at the first hole, the explosion had churned up the ground, tearing up and breaking trees and bushes for several yards around. Back there, however, the pressure had been reduced since the explosion and the gases were being exhaled only slowly and lazily. Here they were coming out under such force that one thought of a giant's blow-pipe.

Returning to the fringe of the 1938 flow, a little further along we discovered another blow-pipe, this time one with three mouths. The gases were coming up with a certain degree of virulence, whistling and snoring through the three adjoining vents, which were four or five inches in diameter. One was like a miniature version of the vent we had already seen: an irregular hole between the unstable blocks of the old lava. The two others, however, were curiously original in appearance: the channels through which the gases were escaping and bursting into flame as they came into contact with the oxygen in the air were nothing less than two of those hollow plaster-casts left as memorials of the charred trees! These tubes of dark, porous stone were today conducting blue, tapering flames, a foot or two long, towards the sky. The upper edge of these mouths was cherry red, the interior an intense yellow. Some extraordinary fluke had made these gases come bursting up through the ground in 1948 exactly under the tree-trunks that had been fossilised ten years earlier.

Drenched from the rain, constantly stumbling in the mud and the sly pot-holes of this volcanic terrain, we continued to advance through the bush. We were getting tired and our feet were beginning to drag. At several fresh points we discovered more traces of brief explosions—the same churned-up ground and the same destruction of vegetation that we had found before. The holes that remained open had a width varying from six inches to fifteen feet. The broadest were all extinct already. Through the narrowest there was generally a jet of burning gas still issuing.

Dusk was approaching, so we swung away to the north and finally reached the rough slope of Mount Rugwété, which made us gasp quite a bit after the hard trip we had had. But that evening, once we had changed into dry clothes and soothed our appetites, we could enjoy the spectacle to be seen from the door of our tent: scores of fires sprinkled out over a distance of about ten miles to the south, right over to Kituro, which was flaring away in the darkness.

These many new vents—through which it was only gas that escaped—peg out the definite line of a crack, or rather, a network of straight parallel cracks, opening between Kituro and the south-eastern foot of gigantic Nyamlagira. Although their general direction forms an angle of about fifty degrees with that of the original great fracture—which heralded the Kituro eruption—they can still be regarded as having been only a belated manifestation of the same phenomenon.[1]

The analysis of the Kituro and the Muhuboli lavas which I had done, a little later on, by the chemists of the geological laboratory at Coste did in fact show that they were identical with those emitted by Nyamlagira, both in the course of its last eruption and during those that had preceded it. Our volcano was thus a child of Mount Nyamlagira, after all, and not one of Niragongo's.

I should say that I was rather pleased with this evidence, for a short time earlier I had had to listen to sweeping assertions about the new volcano's kinship with Niragongo. The person who held this view assured me that the two

[1] *See* Appendix I (e).

volcanoes were connected by a system of underground channels.[1]

[1] My interlocutor, who was so thoroughly convinced of his own scientific perspicacity that I decided it would be no use arguing with him, even claimed to have observed correlated variations in the activity of the two volcanoes . . . Now, it is impossible for magma to circulate underground through such a system of pipes for the simple reason that below a very slight depth its rigidity is such that it can no longer move faster than several millimetres, or, at most, several centimetres, each day. Hence, even if we grant the hypothesis of such interconnections, the slowness with which the subterranean magma would move along them would exclude any possibility that the activity of one vent could be caused by a *simultaneous* diminution in the activity of the other.

CHAPTER XI

NIGHT FALLS TOO SOON

RICHARD left, to return to his plantation in Kenya, and I went back to my Kituro.

Kituro was quieting down more and more, so much so, indeed, that the elephants were coming back, and so were the pygmies, the only human inhabitants of that part of the bush. Incidentally, we were fortunate to fall in with a pygmy one day when we had lost our way.

These tiny people, who live almost exclusively by hunting, are extremely primitive and rather pathetic.

The little men are very timid and are afraid not only of the whites but also of all the other natives. They have an odd way of procuring the few essential foodstuffs that they lack: as night falls, they venture forth to the outskirts of some Bantu village and hang some haunches of venison from the branches of a tree. Twenty-four hours later they come back to the same spot to collect the produce that has been left there in exchange: salt, manioc flour, bananas, beans. Their language is completely different from the Bantu dialects, so that it is difficult to make oneself understood by them, even through the mediation of natives, except by gestures.

The pygmy, whose toes, I was horrified to see, had been almost completely eaten away by jiggers (parasites which penetrate the skin under the nails), left us the moment he had put us back on the right road—'us' being my companion, de Wilde, and myself. Mount Muhuboli, which we reached about four o'clock, was on the way to becoming extinct. We paid it a hasty visit only, but the discovery of a magnificent *pongo* antelope, more than a yard round the withers, wedged in one of the crevasses that slashed the outflows of lava, held us up for a while. We had to cut the poor beast's carotid artery to save it from a death of slow agony. There were only two hours of daylight left and we had almost two miles to cover—rough going over the 1938 lava—before reaching the neighbourhood of Saké.

We were hurrying along as fast as we could over these jagged surfaces, but I was handicapped by a hurt knee, the result of a fall the previous night.

After thirty minutes I said:

'Leave me here and go ahead, will you?'

'I shouldn't dream of it!'

'No, really. You'll be able to get to the village before dark. Then you can send men out with torches.'

Hobbling along after de Wilde, I soon lost sight of him. The two Negroes who were following us were still slower, being loaded up with about a hundred and eighty pounds of antelope meat. 'No go lose so much fine meat,' they had announced firmly.

I was finding it more and more painful to walk. My left leg happens to be something of a surgical exhibit: it has been broken twice, the knee has been dislocated, the foot instantaneously 'peeled' when I accidentally stepped into a hot spring in Katanga, and finally—last but by no means least—just to keep up the tradition I had had the same foot blown more or less to pieces by an unlucky gun-shot!

At dusk, after deciding to hide their booty in a crevice, the two boys joined up with me and we pushed on in darkness. I was convinced it was the darkest night of the entire year; the sky was very low, covered with heavy clouds that sometimes dissolved into a faint drizzle, and just to make things worse, it was the time of the new moon. The last straw was that even the glare of the volcanoes had let us down. Niragongo, over fifteen miles away, was mantled in cloud; Kituro, nearly six miles nearer, was fading out and indicating its presence by nothing more than a red mouth, which sent up so much low-hanging vapour that there was no reflected glare; Muhuboli appeared to be dead. Far ahead of us there did seem to be something like a bush-fire, but it only served to blind us. Visibility was nil. We could not move ahead except by groping along the ground before *every step*. The crevasses and other usual obstacles on lava flow, which are easy enough to get round or jump over when one can see something of where one is going, now became deadly snares. As soon as we discovered an opening in the ground we had to sit down, and then, keeping a firm hold, explore the drop with one foot. I felt rather like a timid bathing-beauty testing the cold waters of the river with one toe. Even the natives, whose sight is naturally much more acute than ours, could make out no more than I could. Every step, every detour, every descent and every climb had to be done by groping and fumbling.

We stopped at frequent intervals to try and get a few minutes' sleep, lying on our backs or curled up like gun-dogs under the drizzle. We were at once discovered by the mosquitoes, those abominable insects which need no light! I tried to stop my ears in order, at least, not to hear them. I tried to slaughter some of them, in my wrath, but succeeding only in giving myself five or six thorough slaps, I abandoned my dreams of resting and resumed the heart-breaking toil onwards.

'Men not coming with light?'

What answer could I give my dear good Paya? I was looking out for them no less impatiently than he was.

After some time he suggested:

'Perhaps those men frightened of elephants.'

Every now and again we uttered shouts for help. There was never any answer. I wondered what had happened to my companion, who had told me that he was utterly incapable of finding his way in the dark . . .

And so, on all fours, on our behinds, and in various other ways too, for all I know, we took *ten hours* to cover the single mile which had separated us from the road when we were overtaken by darkness!

It was four o'clock in the morning when we at last reached it, to our unspeakable relief. Some minutes later we arrived at the village and flopped down in a native hut. We were too tired even to sleep. The thick-walled hut with its rush-thatched roof was perfectly comfortable, all the same. Separated from us by a bamboo partition-wall were some odoriferous goats, which stirred for a short time. I had been given a sort of deckchair made of wood and cow-hide, and this, together with three low solid wooden stools occupied by our host and the two boys, and a dozen baked earthenware pots, pitchers and basins, constituted all the furniture of the room. On the ground between us was a little fire in which three branches, arranged star-wise, were softly glowing to ash, the smoke escaping (more or less) through the opening in the pointed top of the thatched roof. Now and again one of the natives would make some brief remark in a low voice.

We went out a little before dawn and almost at once met with the porters whom we had sent straight on to Saké.

'Where is M. de Wilde?'

'Don't know, Bwana.'

I was filled with frightful anxiety. I had been assuming that my companion, having reached the village before me, had for some reason, such as a lack of torches, found it impossible to send out help to me as arranged. Now I discovered that he had never got here at all! And yet at nightfall he could not have been more than a few hundred yards from the road. If he had had no worse misfortune than to break a leg in a crevasse, that would not be so very serious, but he might just as well have tumbled headlong over one of the innumerable precipices slicing the lava plain and have been killed outright. What was to be done? We must fan out, like beaters, over a front a mile or so long and explore the area he should have crossed. And hope for the best, that was all . . .

We left the village. But just at the moment when we were about to go into action, we saw de Wilde's tall, slender figure coming towards us. I have rarely felt so relieved!

Overtaken by nightfall less than two hundred yards from his goal, and absolutely blind in the darkness, the unfortunate man could only crouch down at the bottom of a fissure. It was a wise solution, however uncomfortable his bivouac might be. Having nothing on but a thin rubber waterproof over his shorts and linen shirt, he had spent the night shivering in the drizzle and the draughts.

'Do you mean to say you didn't hear us? We shouted ourselves hoarse.'

'Well, what do you think I was doing? I shouted regularly every five minutes.'

'But we passed within two hundred yards of your hole. We weren't exactly running, either . . .'

This had clearly been the result of some acoustic peculiarity due to the structure of the cranny in which de Wilde was crouching. I thought of what had happened to the Alpinist Guy Labour, who fell into a crevasse on the glacier of les Nantillons and whose cries were not heard by the rescue-party, although he himself could distinctly hear them coming and going. He was not discovered until eleven days later, fortunately still alive.

CHAPTER XII

THE RED SAUCEPAN BOILS OVER

I HAD come back to Kituro.

One morning, round about five, I was wakened by a strange noise. It was a kind of heavy thudding, such as might have been produced by a herd of antelopes galloping through the bush. Sitting on the edge of my camp-bed, still half asleep, I tried to make out what it was. Wasn't it rather more like the noise of a great fire? But the night, now paling into dawn, held no glimmer of a reflection apart from the usual red glare from the crater.

So then I decided it must be a strong wind. It seemed to be blowing from the northern foot of Kituro. By this time the daylight had increased and I watched, fascinated but slightly disturbed, the leaves fluttering in the thin scrub which separates my camp from the active zone. The trees stirred with mild indifference in the early morning breeze.

I wondered fleetingly if it might be a herd of elephants stampeding, but the minutes passed with no sign of trees being broken. Besides, the noise was not moving, whereas elephants generally move with amazing speed. Turning my head, I saw that Paya and Kaniepala, squatting in the doorway of their wattle hut, were gazing steadily in the direction from which the sound came.

'You think something, Paya?'

He did not answer except by opening his eyes very wide and lifting his shoulders slightly, holding his open hands

palm upward, away from his sides. It was perfect panto-
mime for: 'I don't know.'

There was no doubt about it, it could not be anything
but some sort of volcanic upheaval. Would it not be better
to strike camp and move back some distance? I thought
of the chances of a new outburst, or a new fracture, accompanied by a local earthquake.

Perhaps . . . But if I wanted to be sure about it I would
have to go and take a look.

Dressing in two minutes, grabbing the knapsack and
Rolleiflex, I dashed off along the trail, followed by Paya
carrying the ciné-camera and the instruments. The tall
grasses, heavy with dew, sagged across the narrow track.
The sticky, elastic threads of spiders' webs wrapped themselves round our bare legs and stuck to our faces the
moment we stopped shielding them with our arms.

The further we pressed on, the louder the noise became.
It was now rather like the furious escape of steam from
some immense locomotive with pressure up.

The winding path had brought us out of the forest, to
the fringe of the lava. We went a hundred yards further.
The noise became deafening. Soon we discovered its cause:
between the foot of Kituro and two great walls of agglomerate, stretching away to the north, was a line of little
cones, five to ten feet high, of the kind technically known
as spatter-cones. And out of the top of each of them,
forcibly expelled by the gases whistling up through the
incandescent opening, pasty lumps of red lava were flying
up into the air.

We made our way into the maze formed by the congealed
lava, cautiously approaching these new phenomena. Did
their appearance herald a recrudescence of activity?

The little cones, eight in number, were strung out along
a yawning fissure, a good three feet wide, which had
opened up in the shell of the 'pillow' lava stretching northwards from the foot of Kituro. Two of them seemed to be
already extinct, but the others were blowing off with
furious intensity. However, it was neither difficult nor

dangerous to approach them, for the showers of clots they were throwing out were not too densely concentrated for one to dodge them, with a little agility. The most active cone must have been about seven feet high. Flaring gases were shooting out of the top; the temperature of these flames rose to 960 degrees centigrade, and my little pocket spectroscope revealed the presence of sodium, and possibly also of azote. The new fissure was only letting its gases escape at certain well-defined points, between which it was possible to lean over the black gulf—although of course it was hopeless trying to see anything down there.

But as I was going round one of these spatter-cones, the one nearest to the volcano, I suddenly discovered, less than ten yards away from me, something that was really rather sensational: a kind of basin in which liquid lava was splashing about. It was already covered with a grey, elastic 'skin', very like an elephant's hide, which showed that it was cooling down. This 'skin' would swell up under the pressure of bubbles of gas escaping from the magma, become covered with ripples, rise higher and then fall back with a heavy 'flop'; this agitation was caused by the terrific heavings of the lava immediately underneath it. At every instant the 'skin' would give way at some point, yielding to the pressure of the gases, and a little burst of liquid ash and embers would go up like grape-shot.

I looked about for a higher point from which to observe this pool comfortably; from where I stood at the moment it was only just below the level of my eyes. Making a detour westward round it, I perched on a pile of large boulders, with sulphurous fumes being blown down on me by the prevailing wind. Once again I found myself wavering between a sort of intoxication and the necessity to act. I was worried lest I might not have time to get a thorough impression of this exceptional sight; on the other hand I was in a hurry to take measurements, observe, fix what I saw by getting it down in sketches and photographs.

Really, the thing hardly differed at all from the crucible

of some gigantic blast-furnace. . . . Only, here we were not in a factory; we had penetrated into the inmost secrets of the earth we live on. What was frothing about down there was much more than ore that had been melted by the will of man, in a vessel constructed by man. This was the very substance of the earth itself, chopping about with terrible placidity on the surface of a kind of well that I could feel in my very bowels was beyond all human measuring—fathomless indeed.

The mind finds it easy enough to imagine depths of ten, a hundred, or even a thousand miles. We talk quite light-heartedly about what goes on in the 'discontinuity' of the centre of the earth, some eighteen hundred miles below the surface we walk on. But if we all at once find ourselves in the physical presence of such abysses, our intellectual cocksureness simply evaporates: the might of Nature herself seizes us in her unreasoning claw. The panic lying in ambush just below the surface of the skin is not the same as the terror a soldier feels, flat on his face in a foxhole, with shells crashing steadily all around him; nor is it the terror of a man cowering behind a wall, inwardly praying for the bombs to fall and end the growling of the air-squadrons overhead. Nor is it the same as the shudder the mountaineer feels when he has set out across a field of avalanches and at every step, tight-throated, glances anxiously upward to the heights. No, it is much less clearly defined than any of those terrors. The primitive fear that choked me as I sat by the little pool of lava was less clearly defined, and perhaps more fundamental.

On the edge of the great crater, when the eruption was in full swing, I had never had such a chance as I had now to study my own reactions. Up there I had had to keep far too much on the alert, and all the jumping about I had had to do, because of the violence of the phenomenon, acted as something like an antidote. Here, on the other hand, the calm of this fiery pool, which barely rippled under the ponderous lungings from below, spoke to me in enigmatic terms of a mighty and mysterious power. I was spellbound and literally had to wrench myself out of this fear-laden ecstasy to make myself film the phenomenon. Paya, who had stayed on the other side, seemed equally fascinated.

His amazement was itself something of a miracle for anyone who knew the superb faculty the Negroes have for not being surprised by anything. My good, faithful Paya, who until he became my travelling-companion had never known anything but his native countryside on the banks of the Lualaba, had in the course of a single year discovered the fire in the earth and the snow on the high mountains—snow being something for which his language has not even a name, so that he referred to it either as 'salt' or as 'flour', it didn't matter which. He had helped us build the first igloo just under the Equator, at an altitude of 16,400 feet. He had scorched the soles of his feet in the craters of volcanoes; he had visited lakes covered with hundreds of thousands of pink flamingos and pre-historic sites where men of the early Pleistocene age had hacked their tools and weapons out of the black obsidian lava. He had seen aeroplanes flying and landing and taking off, and had not been particularly astonished since, as he said, the white men had made them for that purpose . . . In almost three years of living together with him I had not been able to catch him in a state of thorough amazement except once: and that was the first time we went to Nairobi, the pleasant capital of Kenya. It was just the time when everyone goes back to work after lunch, and the long lines of little English motor-cars jammed the avenues, a state of traffic congestion unknown in our much more provincial towns in the Congo. These processions of motor-cars made a stupendous impression on Paya! He jumped about in his seat, turning this way and that, and could not stop saying over and over: 'Oh! Bwana! Musu-lulu ya motocara, musululu ya motocara!' ('Oh, Master, how many cars! How many cars!') Although considerably less taken aback by the little pool of lava than by the procession of motor-cars in Nairobi, Paya was looking at it with more than ordinary interest and also, I believe, with terror.

However, I was filming away, very sad at having nothing but an ordinary black-and-white film, when suddenly I saw the grey elephant-hide swell up all over, remain for an instant in that state of turgescence, overbrimming the rim of the basin by some ten or twelve inches, and then all at once overflow in two streams, one on my left, one on my right, which poured away at a rate of more than twelve miles an hour.

It was so extraordinarily beautiful that for several seconds I wasn't even frightened! It seemed all right just to wait . . .

At first only some feet wide, the torrents swiftly spread out until one was about twenty feet across, the other sixty or more. The narrower one had cut me off from Paya, the other was spreading out towards the west.

'Run, Bwana! Run!' Paya was yelling at me.

Still, I had to film what was going on. I had to take advantage of the fact that the reel wasn't yet used up. I was two or three feet above the bed of the two new out-flows, which might, of course, at any minute close behind me in a pincer-movement. I made a rapid calculation and decided that there would have to be a quite considerable addition of new magma before that happened. If there should be such an additional boiling-over, I would still have time to escape on to the old wall of agglomerate which towered up some thirty paces behind me. It was a safe refuge where I would be able to hold out until the new out-flows had formed a crust strong enough for me to walk over.

The film was finished! Two, just two more photographs. Then, swinging round, I beat a retreat to the wall. On the other side of the river of fire Paya ran along parallel with me, looking anxious. The lava had passed the wall and was trickling on beyond it, spreading wider, but its speed was now less than the speed at which a man walks.

The further it spread out, the more it slowed down . . .
Just as well, too!

As soon as I had scrambled up on to my perch, I was
reassured. There to the north was a second wall of agglomerate, of equally ancient date, which would provide me
with a way out. The lava, which had seemed as liquid as
water when the pool overflowed, was now no more than
a viscous fluid. Its speed was no longer more than three
or four miles an hour.

I had simply not had time to take the temperature at the
beginning of the phenomenon. The colour of the lava,
which was yellowish, suggested it had been nearly 1,100
degrees centigrade. Now it was bright cherry-red, gushing
out of the pit at 1,030 degrees.

Very quickly, as it came into contact with the air, a
skin formed, at first dimming and then entirely veiling
the brightness of the incandescent paste. Thirty yards or
so away, the elastic skin had already hardened into a rigid
crust, which was quite opaque. And yet underneath the
molten lava was still flowing on, seeping through the
cracks and now and then licking out over the fringe—at
the sides and in front—in scarlet bubbles that became
larger and larger until they too were covered with a rigid
crust. This process made it possible for the new lava to
keep on spreading further and further.

I made a detour northwards round the eastern outflow
and rejoined Paya. He seemed relieved. A warm surge of
gratitude rose within me to see how concerned he had
been as to my fate. Good old Paya with his friendly face
under the white cap he was so proud of! Every fresh
adventure did a little more to make the servant he had
been in the beginning into a real friend.

By the next day the gaseous vents were quieting down.
The pointed flames, like those of a gas-burner, had made

way for lazy bluish fumes that came drifting up from the orifices. The ejection of clots of lava had completely ceased.

However, activity began again several hours afterwards.

At first I could not succeed in discovering any regular rhythm in these manifestations, but after several times an amazing regularity suddenly set in, which was maintained for forty hours: there was a paroxysm lasting about two minutes, followed by a seventeen minutes' lull. I could not find any explanation for this strict precision except some mechanism analogous to that which regulates geysers.[1]

It was several weeks before the new outflows, which had been steadily slowing up all along their front-lines, could cover the surrounding area, and so I had plenty of time to become familiar with them.

So long as I had the wind at my back, it was possible to come up to within a pace of the front of the outflow. It was pretty hot, of course, but one could just stand it . . . One day Paya and I made use of the lava in this way for frying our eggs.

Another day, while exploring 'my' new outflows—for I had come to regard this volcano and all its manifestations as being my private property—I came upon an extraordinarily lovely sight.

The lava was moving on in its usual way, seeping along under the newly formed shell, which was constantly trying

[1] The reader will be aware that geysers, which are only to be found in volcanic areas, are jets of hot water and steam that shoot up vertically, sometimes to a great height, at more or less regular intervals. They are probably due to pressure from the gases rising from the depths and escaping through a network of fractures. In certain places these gases cannot escape freely on account of a double hair-pin bend, i.e. a bend that is Z-shaped, in which atmospheric water, or water from the underground water-level, accumulates. These gases, however, keep on rising, gradually pushing the column of water up the terminal tube. When the liquid at the base has passed the second bend, the gases, the pressure of which is greater than that of the atmosphere combined with the weight of the liquid column, suddenly and violently pass through the water, sweeping it up into the air with them. This is the eruption of the geyser. After this violent discharge a period of calm sets in, during which the water again seals up the conduit, forcing the magmatic gases to accumulate behind it.

to hold it back. Here, however, the front had reached the upper edge of a sheer drop over rock, some fifteen or twenty feet deep, and the molten paste, after flowing gently to the edge of the cliff, suddenly plunged into the void in a cascade of fire—but in slow-motion, which gave it a fantastic appearance. It did not *fall*; it was a viscous sheet descending like a curtain. Nevertheless, this vertical descent was too rapid for a crust to form on it. Only at the

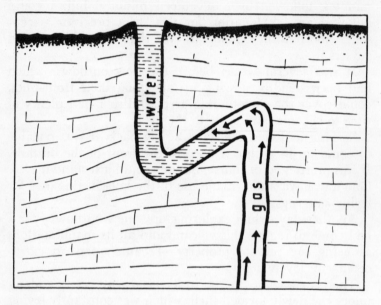

bottom a thin elastic skin dimmed the red of this strange drop-curtain.

Two other flows, about six or eight feet wide, like the first, reached the same cliff, and went down side by side in two new cascades.

The light veil caused by the cooling process gradually thickened towards the base, where it became a grey blanket, though still plastic. Drawn along by the current of the paste below, it wrinkled up into transverse ripples, curling and twisting in a last fling of plastic freedom, and finally produced something resembling thick cables,

A volcanic bomb of solid lava, flattened out on impact with the earth.
(*Tazieff—Congopresse*)

A deep fracture between the crater of the old volcano, Nyamlagira, and
Tshabene, the new one to which it gave birth in 1948. (*Tazieff*)

Kituro: an explosion of lava in the crater, seen at night. (*Tazieff*)
Below, flows of creeping, incandescent lava. (*Tazieff*)

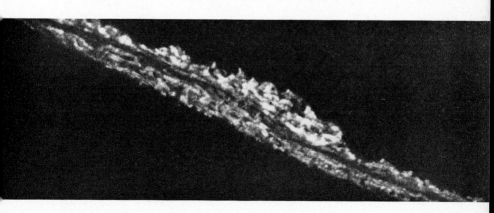

Shabubembe, a new crater, erupted in 1951 and in three months poured out more than 45 million cubic feet of lava. (*Congopresse*)

As Kituro's red-hot lava pours into Lake Kivu, natives collect half-boiled fish on the surface. (*Tazieff*)

The waters of Kivu boiling around lava as it enters the lake.
(Tazieff-Congopresse)

Climbing Mount Etna. (*Picciotto*)

Haroun Tazieff ten feet away from the active crater of Mount Etna.

(*Picciotto*)

bluish grey-black in colour. I was seeing with my own eyes the formation of the celebrated *corded* or *ropy* lava that in Hawaii is called *pahoehoe* and in Iceland *helluhraun* . . . Sometimes, however, this corded crust would split and the incandescent magma would ooze out through the cracks. The cliff with the three cascades gave off a wonderful red glow. At eight paces I could only just stand the dazzling glare of the stuff trickling down there at a temperature of more than a thousand degrees centigrade. I had to fall back once, and then again, before the torrents that, once they found themselves once more on even ground, suddenly lunged out at me with horrible tentacles. Over the top of the cliff the viscous lava came flowing on and on inexorably, with no sound but a faint hissing.

It struck me that here was the origin of the stories about dragons that are to be found in so many different mythologies, originating in so many different parts of the world.

The ancient Greeks saw the gluey lava of Etna, Stromboli, and Santorin. Is not the Hydra herself, ceaselessly renewed as she is, that crimson outflow whose black shell hardens so that for a fleeting moment one hopes it is halted, only to see the burning heads re-appearing here and there, snapping forward, still there in spite of every obstacle? The Japanese, the Chinese, all the nations of the Far East, also knew the horror of those hundred-headed monsters. The Scandinavians themselves saw them loom up, more appalling than ever, in the gloom of the Polar winter.

One morning I found myself face to face with one of these *bestes feu jetant*, to use Villon's words. Its flaming jaws were opened wide, motionless, straight opposite me. The scarlet throat emitted slow gasps. I saw the torrid mucus palpitating, while the sulphurous breath was exhaled in purple volutes. Pointed, mobile fangs ran along its lips of fire. At some moments its fury seemed to be allayed, or perhaps it was gathering strength for the next onslaught; at such times the swollen tongue slid back into the throat and the canines that had been jutting towards their prey collapsed, inert. But it was only a moment before those atrocious jaws opened wide again, and the fangs darted forward . . .

It was no more than the gaping orifice of a spatter-cone, and I was a modern geologist, right in the middle of the atomic age: there wasn't much chance for the supernatural to get the better of me. But what would my thoughts have been, what terror, what looming vague dread would have stirred in me at such an encounter if I had been a shepherd from the Campagna or a Sicilian sailor three thousand years ago, on the slopes of some Mediterranean volcano?

How should I have described it, telling the story afterwards, but as a *dragon*?

CHAPTER XIII

A DESCENT INTO NIRAGONGO

FOR MONTHS, during which I had been exploring the district all round Kituro and Muhuboli, I had been casting covetous glances at their gigantic neighbour, Niragongo. I had already climbed it, but all I had been able to see from the edge of the enormous cauldron on its summit was vapour and smoke. Three or four attempts to get down into it had been made without success. It was regarded as settled that there *was* no going down into it: it was too steep and there was too much gas . . . All the same, in looking round I had seen what seemed to be a possible way down the almost vertical walls, and in the five months that I had been living in the midst of volcanic emanations I had got to know what they were like. So long as one kept out of the immediate neighbourhood of the vents emitting them—in other words, so long as they were diluted with water-vapour and air—these fumes were not toxic to a fatal degree. As for the descent being declared vertical—it was all of fifteen degrees less than that! It was not so very long ago since my Savoyard friends and I had been climbing rock-face of quite a different order! I was certain that I would at least be able to reach a promontory jutting out about half or two-thirds of the way down. After that, nobody could know what it would be like . . .

I had no difficulty in persuading Tondeur, a friend from
Coste, to rope up with me in a first attempt to make the
descent. A big, broad-shouldered man, Tondeur seemed
to have the steady hands and the cool head indispensable
to such an undertaking. And so the thing was undertaken
in June, and went off in the following manner . . .

We were now in the dry season. In the noon-day light,
the string of porters, balancing packages on their heads,
wound their way along through the tall grasses waving
in the wind. Ahead of us, nearly 10,000 feet up, rose the
base of the mighty cone.

At an altitude of 6,500 feet we came into the very dense,
almost completely dark forest that covers the lower part
of the mountain. The only way of advancing through this
fiendishly tangled jungle was along the elephant tracks.
We clambered over huge fallen tree-trunks, and we crawled
on all fours under trees whose fall had been stopped at half
a man's height from the ground by scrub and creepers.

At first we kept plunging up to the knees in mud, that
black *potopoto* in which nettles abound—and what nettles!
Higher up the ground became drier and the incline sharper.

Four o'clock. We come out at last into a clearing amidst
the gigantic brambles. Here we shall pitch our camp, a
tent for Tondeur and me, two wattle huts for the natives.

The men have already lit fires. The porters' beans are
boiling in a big old aluminium saucepan, our boys'
manioc is simmering on a second fire, and the white men's
'chop' (food) on a third. Inside the huts there are yet
more fires burning, sending up thick blue coils of smoke.
All this damp wood smokes so much that it makes our
eyes water—a foretaste of the acrid vapours we shall get
our fill of in the crater.

Turning the last two hours of daylight to account, we

make a quick push higher up the mountain. After coming out of the last thicket of brambles, we leave the forest behind. Henceforth the dominant note is rock. There are still some lobelias, tall candle-like things standing up on the black stone, and then, between 10,800 and 11,500 feet, there are only the bare cliffs, which are fluted by huge ribs of basalt radiating out towards the base.

The crater! Amid the vapours we see the route, the first few hundred feet of the descent. We establish the fact that it is impossible to get along the knife-edge ridge surrounding the cauldron; so there is no other way to be considered. This route itself makes 'recalls' by fixed rope quite out of the question; there is not the slightest ledge to which one can fix anything.

The night was cold and very damp. Humidity is the main characteristic of the high mountains along the Equator. The air is constantly saturated with moisture, to such a point that wherever the ground is not porous (and fortunately it is, on the volcanoes that are not too much eroded) it is transformed into a peat-bog.

At nine o'clock in the morning we were back on the summit and once more staring down into the vast sink-hole. Part of the 'floor' was visible today. The centre seemed to be pierced by a wide shaft, the south-eastern rim of which we could see; the other two-thirds of the orifice were veiled from sight by a terrific column of vapour. At our feet the walls surrounding the sink-hole were made up of horizontal strata alternating with tuff and outflows, gashed by vertical *dikes* of hard rock. To the south, one of these dikes ran right up from the bottom to the crest on which we were standing. It seemed to me a magnificent climb—very 'artificial', of course, necessitating the use of iron eye-bolts and rope yokes—but certainly a climb up well worth doing some day. However, for the present it was a matter of first getting down.

Paya handed me the haversack. I got out the rope, that good old rope of mine that had not been used for years now. It was exciting to feel its precious suppleness against the palm of my hand, and its delightful smell, which always made me think of a little village store in Savoyd with loaves of bread, candles, string, goloshes and materials, all jumbled up together and everything smelling of everything else . . .

At that moment the worthy head keeper of the National Park at last realised that we had not come up to the top of the volcano to have a look over the edge in the usual tourist way, but that we really meant to go down. The day before when we had explained our plans to him, he had seemed to approve. Was it a misunderstanding? Was he playing for time? Whatever the cause, today he broke into cries of distress, explaining volubly that there was every reason why such a descent was impossible: the devils haunting the craters, the dangers of the tottering edges of the wall, and of poisonous gases, and above all the sacrosanct regulations of the National Park of which he was the authorised representative here.

On this last point I quelled his doubts by showing him an official letter with a grand printed letter-head, authorising me to go wherever I wished to in the Park, so long as it was in connection with volcanology. The letter-head alone would obviously have done the trick, for the aged worthy knew no word of French. It was a waste of time trying to make him understand that the danger of the descent was merely apparent and that we would take it on ourselves to look after the devils: I could not set his mind at rest. So there were four faces furrowed with anxiety watching us as we roped ourselves together and cautiously began that 'infernal' descent.

The three first rope-lengths (we had left fifteen yards between us) were easy. The only delicate operation was finding holds: whatever their shape and size, they generally gave way at once. Then we had to clear the first considerable stratum of tuff that we came to—those very fine yellowish volcanic ashes interspersed with blocks of various sizes. Fortunately this dust had agglomerised and become cemented by the action of rain-water; the weight of the strata above had rammed it down and given this rock, once entirely unstable, a certain degree of solidity. By gingerly making use of the jagged places shaped by erosion, and sometimes cutting steps for ourselves as though in hard snow, we made headway without any real difficulties, though not without a certain amount of nervous tension. There was no chance of exchanging reassuring and encouraging remarks; and each of us knew that if one fell, he would bring the other down with him. On the other hand, the psychological effect of the length of hemp that turns two climbers into a 'party' was very great: I would certainly not have risked the climb on my own.

A little while later we reached the famous promontory that Tondeur had christened the 'spur of hesitation', an enormous ledge measuring several cubic yards, embedded in a stratum of tuff. We picked our way round it with due care and could then see the rest of our route. It needed only a few seconds to set our minds at rest: although the lower part was steeper than the wall we had just come down, it looked no less practicable. The riskiest stage would certainly be crossing the two very wide strata of tuff. As for the outflows, they were very solid rock and offered enough holds for us to get across them, in spite of their being almost vertical.

Here we could sit down. We took the opportunity to have a snack. As we looked down, the floor of the cauldron seemed much nearer to us now and we could distinctly see a plain of grey lava streaked with long black concentric fissures running round the big central shaft. It was from this shaft that the mighty column of smoke rose incessantly. Fortunately the wind was driving it away from us.

We had scarcely got going again when the wind changed,

wrapping us in a sulphurous fog. We had equipped ourselves with gas-masks. Tondeur stopped to put his on,
but since what we were breathing seemed a very pale
imitation of what I had more than once encountered on
Kituro, I went on down with my nostrils disdainfully free.

We now had to swing towards the right in order to get
across a stratum of tuff more than thirty feet deep, which
luckily was not very steep. There we noticed some of those
little 'fairy chimneys' or 'crowned columns' that the
process of erosion cuts out of the soft rock under a protective

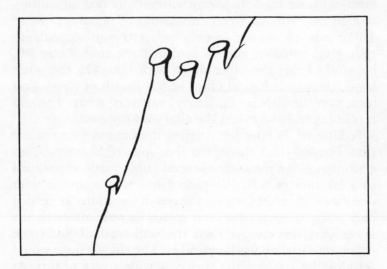

mass of harder rock. The water draining from the cliff,
or the rain, wears the soft rock away round the hard rock,
so that the latter is soon left in relief, and when the ground
keeps disappearing under the action of rain and storm
washing it away, the rock is soon left standing out further
and further from its immediate surroundings, a sort of
hat on an embryo column that in several centuries may
reach a height of sixty feet.[1] Here these stones were no

[1] An analogous phenomenon is sometimes observed on glaciers, where
drift-blocks protect the ice underneath from the heat of the sun, so that at the
end of the summer these rocks are left perched on the top of a short column
of ice.

larger than one's fist, or even smaller, and the chimneys were no more than a foot high.

A hard lava flow made us work our way back to the left, after which we had to go obliquely to the right to get across another stratum of light-coloured, crumbling tuff. Then came a series of fairly thin superimposed layers of lava, evidence of a period when there had been a rapid succession of emissions of lava. All along our descent we could read in this way the history of the last centuries of the volcano's life: outflow, great explosion, big outflow, less concentrated outflows, explosion of less intensity, very big outflow, explosions . . . and so on.

And then there we were! We got a foothold on the summit of a heap of stones that had crumbled down and from there, without stopping to take precautions, we ran full tilt down on to the floor of the sink-hole. It had taken us over three hours.

Once we had unroped, we slapped each other on the back with great heartiness, exulting over our magnificent effort! Coming down, all in all, had been easy. But what really made us ecstatic was the thought that we were the first to get here and that we had done so after all the experts had declared the place inaccessible!

The vapours did not trouble us. Tondeur took off his gas-mask. His brown eyes sparkled. The breeze blew a few stray locks of hair across his forehead.

The floor was composed of the type of lava known as 'pillow' lava, very slightly rippled, the hollows filled up with volcanic sand of the same kind as the tuff in the cliff-face, which had collected at this lower level as a result of erosion and the action of rainfall.

There was no familiar object to give us any sense of scale. The walls seemed vertiginous: the jagged cliff-top was outlined against the sky far above. Around us there was nothing but this sealed-off world, enclosed by immense cliffs, only a section of its grey area appearing between the walls and the fumes ceaselessly rising from the centre.

We discovered a long volcanic crevasse. It was evident that liquid lava occasionally gushed up out of it, for lumps of lava that had landed still in a pasty state had piled up along the edges; some of them had even piled up to a height of nearly a hundred feet.

Counting our strides, we set out for the central shaft: the distance up to it seemed to be about two hundred yards. When we got to the edge of the vast pit, we found it was impossible to see anything at all: it was completely hidden in eddies of grey fumes.

From far above we heard shouts. We raised our heads. Tiny silhouettes were making movements up there: our native companions had come to look over the edge of the cauldron and were hailing our reappearance and the success of the enterprise.

We then gave our minds to working out the height of the surrounding walls by various methods. Tondeur went back, counting his long strides as far as the foot of the cliff, and I did some rough calculations of angles, starting from a base a hundred paces long—all quite approximate, of course. Finally we worked out that six hundred to seven hundred and fifty feet would probably be not too remote from reality.

Once again we arrived at the shaft. Lying flat on our bellies on the edge of it, we strained our eyes in vain to see anything beyond a few vague outlines of grey rocks blurred by vapours. . . . Suddenly a sharp gust of wind from the north swept the moving smoke-screen aside for several seconds. We got a clear view of the crater itself.

It was in the shape of a gigantic cylinder about a quarter of a mile in diameter, the sides practically vertical. But it was the sight at the bottom, about five or six hundred feet down, that was amazing: in its north-western quarter there was a lake of live lava, boiling away ceaselessly from the action of forces deep below; every now and then the

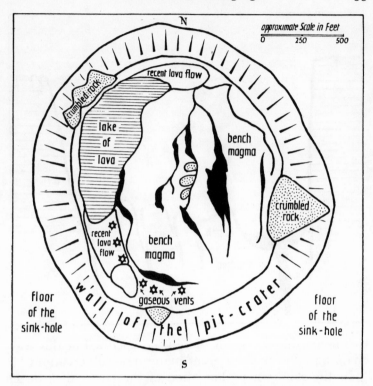

elastic black skin covering it burst and threw up fountains of cherry-red lava, while at the southern end a tremendous froth of liquid fire lashed the banks with heavy scarlet waves.

This lake was the shape of a half-moon, a hundred yards long and a hundred and fifty yards across at the widest point.

While we were filming this extraordinary spectacle the lava suddenly overflowed the limits of the lake and we saw it moving on, swiftly, and silently, a sort of long tongue that in a few moments had covered a surface of more than an acre. Then the vapours spread out again, once more hiding the depths of the crater from view. But by a stroke of good luck the wind came to our aid, and during the

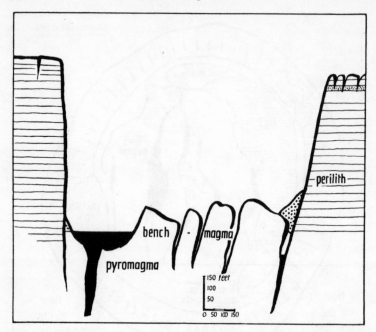

two hours that we spent there it co-operated in this way, enabling us to make a great many more observations.

In the southern prolongation of the lake half a dozen little cones jutted up, some yards in height, continually spitting out gases, vapours and virulent jets of black smoke. Sometimes they puffed comparatively quietly, sometimes again with such violence that one felt inclined to believe some living creature in paroxysms of rage was blowing these jets up from below.

The zone of chief activity was in the western part of the depths. The rest was made up of that 'dead' lava to which the celebrated American volcanologist Jaggar gave the name of *bench magma*. It formed a sort of gigantic staircase, each tread of which was a real cliff. Between these escarpments yawned abysses out of which slow fumes curled up.

I studied the surroundings of the shaft itself with impassionate attentiveness, hoping to be able to make out a way to go down it. But the examination did not reveal anything very promising. The only hope lay in having oneself let down, either *en rappel* or by means of a windlass, till one reached the top of a pile of debris heaped up against the eastern part of the wall, and then to make use of that debris to get down to the bottom. But in any case we were not equipped for an adventure of that kind.

The climb up the cliff round the cauldron was, of course, much less difficult than the descent. It is always incomparably easier, in rock-climbing, to go up than to go down; furthermore, this time we knew that it could be done.

The welcome we got from our faithful Negroes, patiently waiting at the summit, was in itself a heart-warming reward. They were all benumbed with cold at that altitude —11,400 feet—even though we were on the Equator.

CHAPTER XIV

THE GREAT CAULDRON

KITURO was at its last gasp.

First the incandescent projectiles had ceased, then the emissions of lava. Soon, standing on the edge of the cauldron, one could see nothing more than the gloomy red glare of the conduit, out of which serene blue-grey vapours drifted upward.

Before going back to Europe, my time being up, I decided to pay a visit to my friend Richard, who had asked me to do so. So I set out for Uganda, after having spent three days at Ruanda with other friends, whose plantation is at an altitude of more than 6,500 feet, on the slopes of the Muhavura volcano.[1] In the midst of the pyrethrum fields that rise in terraces up the side of the mountain, I relaxed after the fatigues of a successful climb I had just made in the splendid Mountains of the Moon (Ruwenzori, 16,790 feet).

After that came the endless plains of Uganda's grasslands. Day after day the gently undulating land unrolled before me, all high grasses. Sometimes some shrubby little trees would appear, proteas that were rather like stunted apple trees, parasol acacias, candelabra, euphorbias, and, few and far between, the group of mango-trees and banana-palms that showed where a village nestled. Every hundred and fifty miles or so there would be a station, both European and Indian, administrative and

---

[1] This volcano is regarded, perhaps mistakenly, as extinct.

commercial. White houses, impeccable green lawns, the club, golf-course, tennis-courts—all this at first sight seems extremely English. But contrasting with them, tumble-down hovels with rusty corrugated iron roofs indicate the 'commercial centres' and recall the less attractive aspects of western civilisation.

I was glad to be able to drift along in my motor-car towards that distant home I had left over three years before. I had not yet reached the stage of missing the presence of the tactful and devoted Paya . . . Paya was now with my friend Godenne. Circumspect as ever, he had not accepted the proposal to enter Godenne's service until he had spent long days and long nights living with him and me on the sides of Mount Ruwenzori. From the doorway of the little refuge at an altitude of 14,900 feet he had watched us set out on the last climb, and then had waited for us for the thirty-two hours that the trip had taken. On our return he had welcomed us with his broad smile and a terrific potful of stew of his own invention. After that he had agreed to change masters.

We shook hands, and for the last time I looked into Paya's honest eyes.

'Well, Paya, a good homekeeping.'

'A good journey, Bwana. If you come back to Congo, you call me.'

Richard's plantation is tucked away in the wonderful cedar forest 6,500 feet up the steep scarp of the Great Rift Valley.

This gigantic chasm, a good many miles across and several hundred feet deep, runs right down the east of Africa, from Ethiopia to the southern part of Tanganyika. In the plains on each side of it volcanoes have come through here and there, as a result of secondary fractures. Among these are the extinct giants of Elgon and Mount Kenya. But the Rift itself is riddled with volcanic hills.

And from the house that Richard built himself (with timber from his own cedars) the view dips straight down into an immense cauldron. Vast as it looked from the house, I was nevertheless considerably surprised when my friend told me that it was six miles across. This was Menengai, an enormous hollow, in places a thousand feet deep, which is probably the result of the explosion that burst the original cone. This volcano is now dormant, and all that comes out of the crater is some drifting white vapours.

Seen from above, the whole bottom of the crater seemed to be horizontal, but it was in fact a succession of valleys and hills, with several gorges and cliffs scarring them. I realised this next day when, having come down from our heights, we went through a wide breach in the wall into the interior of that shut world. What had looked to me like low-growing vegetation turned out to be a relatively dense jungle, with some quite big trees. Almost at once we lost all sense of being inside a crater.

Richard led us along a trail that he knew well, having gone along it many a time.

'I pay regular visits to this cauldron,' he said.

'As the family doctor?'

'You might put it like that. I take its temperature—that's to say, the temperature of the vapours. If it ever had any idea of waking up, I should be the first to know. And in good time!'

I thought I could hear a faint undertone of gravity in my friend's voice. I thought of the town of St. Pierre, which had been wiped out because people had not known, or had not wanted to know, how to tell what was going to happen, and a picture flitted across my mind of something else, very recent indeed—the three enchanting little girls, Josselyne, Viviane and Françoise, who had so gaily shown me round the cowsheds at milking time the day before.

From the top of one of the many nipples that always dot the bottom of a *caldera*, we noticed a wide cranny in the inner cliff. Leaving our track, we quickly climbed up to the entrance to this aperture, which was more than the height of a man and about fifteen paces wide. One of its cavities narrowed down into a gallery, which, in turn, opened out into an almost spherical cavern several yards in diameter. All this had been hollowed out in a bench of lava; but it was very different from the lava that I had got used to in the Virunga Range. It looked like coarse glass, almost black, and with the same conchoidal and glittering faults as the bottom of a broken bottle.

'Yes,' Richard said. 'Obsidian.'

This type of lava is very definitely distinguished from the others by its essentially vitreous and amorphous (that is to say, non-crystalline) character. It is also different from the basaltic rocks I was familiar with, its chemical composition being much richer in silica. There was nothing astonishing about its presence in the gigantic cauldron opened up by the Menengai explosion.[1]

We were certainly not the first human beings to enter this place: the ground was scattered with little fragments of obsidian, and one did not need to be much of an expert to see that they came from the shaping of paleolithic tools. There we were, in fact, right on a prehistoric site, heaven alone knows how many thousands of years old. This place was at once the quarry and the workshop: men of that remote past had hacked out the volcanic glass on the spot, to shape it into their various instruments, axes, spearheads, knives, scrapers. . . . Kenya seems to have been one of the cradles of the human race, and there are many prehistoric sites there. Some weeks previously Richard had had the privilege of being present at the discovery—on an

---

[1] Silicaceous lavas, which are called *acidic* (in contradistinction to the basaltic lavas, which are poor in silica and are called *basic*) are emitted at temperatures generally varying between seven and eight hundred degrees, which is lower than those of the various basalts, and they are much more viscous. Thus they tend to congeal and very quickly seal up the vent that has emitted them. The gases continue to separate and, no longer finding any aperture to escape through, then concentrate until their tension exceeds the power of resistance in the walls of rock in which they are sealed up. An explosion then occurs, making a free passage through the throat of the volcano.

island in Lake Victoria—of a skull that, according to Dr. Leakey, who excavated it—must have belonged to a venerable ancestor of homo sapiens.

The black obsidian outflow in the heart of which we stood was stratified between two layers of grey tuff. Examining this tuff, I discovered some little stony lumps, almost spherical, of the same colour as the mass of the stratum and about the size of large peas. Some of them were slightly flattened; others were more or less pear-shaped. They were raindrops that had been fossilised for many, many thousands of years—raindrops from some terrific equatorial downpour. They must have come down, in the course of an explosive eruption, on the ashes that were accumulating and which were instantly being covered by yet more ashes, so imprisoning the little globules in natural cement, the water itself still fresh. It was a queer feeling to be brought like this into the immediate presence of a fleeting event that had been completed so long ago . . .

We pressed on towards our vapours.

I would never have believed that one could lose one's way in the crater of a volcano. But this one was so huge that we very nearly did so. The savannah and the jungle were soon succeeded by practically insurmountable high banks of scoriaceous lava.

'I don't think I'd like to have to walk in that,' I said, casting a far from favourable glance at one of those jagged-topped black walls. 'I'd rather take a stroll along a garden wall covered with bottle-glass.'

Richard, who was lighting a cigarette, gave a brief smile.

His voice as calm as ever, he replied: 'Imagine what it was like one day when I had to cross one of those outflows.' He made a slight grimace at the corner of his mouth. 'It's an acquaintance I'm not at all set on renewing, I can assure you.'

'You would think they'd been put there just to remind us that we're inside a volcano, and not merely in the bush.'

'Yes. It looks as if everything has been overgrown by the

jungle. But far from it. From where we're going you'll get a general view. Perhaps that'll give you a different idea of it.'

He had already begun to walk on, in his practised way, through the grass and scrub. After some hours in the forest we reached the foot of a fairly large hillock on which the vegetation was much more sparse.

'More recent lava,' I murmured.

From the top of the hillock we could see that we were right in the centre of the immense *caldera*.

'Well?' my companion asked.

I had to admit that in this panorama the green patches of jungle were no more than minor details in the vast volcanic scene. But we had come to investigate the vapours. Richard, to whom I had shown off 'my' Kituro, had to do the honours of his menagerie.

'Your volcanic vapours don't strike me as being very virulent, Richard.'

Their temperatures oscillated around ninety degrees centigrade. 'It hasn't varied for a year now,' Richard admitted. 'Oh well, the volcano remains dormant, that's all.'

'I won't go so far as to say I find it disappointing, but——'

'You'd have liked me to have a little eruption staged for you on your trip to Nakuru? Some other time, perhaps. However, I doubt whether your desire would be shared by the local planters.'

'Or by the inhabitants of Nakuru, for that matter. It's a very nice little town, by the way. But then what's the idea of coming to settle down right at the foot of this redoubtable volcano?'

'You mustn't make too much of a joke of it. Two years ago some Masai nomads who were passing told us there was an eruption going on at Oldonyo Lengai, a hundred miles or so from here, in the southern end of the valley.'

'And so of course you rushed off there?'

'By plane. I went in a little two-seater. It was a mainly

gaseous eruption, without any emission of lava. The explosions were very violent and came in great bursts, throwing up blocks which had been torn out of the sides of the conduit and pulverised. The dust made a dark umbrella, something like a cloud of soot. A superb sight!'

As we were returning to the farm, Richard began telling me about the very numerous volcanoes strung out along the Rift. Some are extinct, but the majority are undoubtedly only in a deceptively dormant state. The most famous of them in Kilimanjaro. With an altitude of approximately 19,700 feet, it is the highest point in Africa. Sometimes, in fine weather, from the direction of Nakuru, or Nairobi, or Voii, or, even better, from the heights of Mount Kenya, one can see a white cloud floating in the blue above the haze on the sky-line. This motionless form is not a cloud at all, but the snowy peak of an incredibly high mountain, looking as though it were suspended in mid-air.

Kilimanjaro has often been spoken of, even in specialists' writings, as though it were an extinct volcano. It is nothing of the kind. Erosion has not damaged the perfection of that colossal cone; its circular crater is still a black abyss marked out against the whiteness of those snow-bound heights; and the volcanic fumes that sometimes begin to puff and stir, the muffled rumblings that are emitted, the earth-tremors that shake it from time to time, are all ample evidence that it is only dormant, and perhaps not even very soundly so. In 1948 this giant began to growl, and the heat given off by the volcanic vapours increased to such an extent that the volume of the glaciers noticeably decreased. But the time was not ripe for an eruption. After some weeks calm reigned once more.

It is not difficult to climb Kilimanjaro; it is simply a test of one's patience. There is a pleasant hotel to stay at, some 6,500 feet above sea-level. From there you get to the top in three stages. First you go through forests, those strange mountain jungles where giant brambles, lobelias, arborescent groundsel, carpets of alchemillas and clumps of immortelles all grow side by side. After about 16,500 feet there is bare rock. Then come the glaciers. Right at the summit there is the large cylindrical pit of the central shaft in the middle of a tremendous sink-hole, the inner wall of which is vertical and rises to a crag only at one point.

Separated from Kilimanjaro by a 'corridor' several miles wide is another volcano, and a very active one, too. This is Meru, 14,700 feet in altitude. It reminds one, though on a grander scale, of Niragongo, with its steep black sides and the lazy vapours escaping from the enormous cauldron gaping in the summit.

I made a trip over to the foot of Meru, and I must admit I should have liked a chance to look inside it. Unfortunately both time and money were running out. It was the same with another volcano, a little further away to the south-west—Ngorongoro, whose *caldera* is probably the largest in Africa, being about twelve miles by ten. They both form part of explorations we have planned for later on, as well as that of Oldonyo and the active volcanoes in the Rift southward of Lake Rodolphe, in the desert areas of Frontier Province. For the moment Richard and I had to content ourselves with working out plans in our heads.

All the same, as we still had a few days on our hands, Richard one evening suggested we should go and explore Lake Hannington at the bottom of the Rift Valley.

CHAPTER XV

HOT SPRINGS AND PINK FLAMINGOS

RICHARD'S Mercury took us northwards over the dusty road that winds along the bottom of the Rift from Nakuru. Here the Rift is about twenty-five miles wide. After we had done twenty miles or so, we left this road and turned off to the right along a track leading through a sisal plantation.

This track very soon branched in various directions and became hardly perceptible at all on the dry earth. At each fork we chose the branch that seemed to be going more or less northward. After driving for some time through grasslands sprinkled with umbrella-shaped bushes, among boulders and occasional clumps of thorny shrubs, we realised that we had made a mistake: our track was taking us further and further eastwards, and even southeastwards. With his usual stolidity, Richard turned the car off the track. After all, there was not much point in following a track when one could just as easily drive over the flat ground of the Rift, tacking between the acacias. It was not long before we met a Masai woman driving a flock of goats ahead of her. Overcome with shyness, not understanding a word of our Swahili nor of our boy's Kikuyu, she retreated without giving us any idea of where we were.

The going was becoming very rough indeed. We had to climb a rocky hill. The car chugged laboriously uphill between the boulders, skidding on the smooth pebbles. Sometimes we had to stop, get out and move a boulder out of the way. At last we reached the top. Then the trouble was coming down the other side. The slope was so steep and the surface so bad—cluttered with pebbles and big stones and potted with holes of every conceivable shape and size—that we were afraid of going too fast even in bottom gear and with the brakes on. However, we pulled through without being any the worse and soon found ourselves on the level ground at the bottom of the valley.

Here we found ourselves entering a vast area without a tree to be seen far and wide. In the midst of it, looking oddly incongruous in those solitary wilds, were two low-built thatched buildings, standing side by side, and a dozen native huts. Stopping the car, we got out, and were immediately blinded by the torrid glare of the early afternoon. The air was a-quiver with heat. There was no shade to be seen except through the openings to the huts. Under a straw awning we saw some Negroes squatting, impassively watching us look around for some local authority. In answer to Richard's repeated calls another native came running out of a hut. He was wearing a khaki duck shirt and shorts in European style, and on his shaven head a peaked cap with a red cross badge on it. He was a medical orderly and told us that this was both the official hospital station and an Indian agency. As Richard had thought, it was easy to get from here to Lake Hannington. We asked the man to get us two or three porters.

'H'mmmm . . . Watu yote hapa, malari. All men here sick.'

But Richard was familiar with the native way of doing things. He knew there always had to be a discussion first.

'Oh yes,' the man admitted, 'there is a little village.'

'Where? Far away?'

'No. Little bit near.'

A little bit near! There is a subtle scale that goes like this: 'all along near', 'little bit near', 'near', 'near-near', 'little bit far away', 'far away', 'much far away', 'all along far away', and 'faaar away . . .' And besides the words themselves there was the mimicry and the intonation! The facial expression, the lifted eyebrows, the furrowed brow, the head thrown back—all this contributed to stressing the emphatic terms. 'M'bali kabisa' meant 'very far away', but 'mbaaali . . .', with suitable grimaces thrown in, might mean 'at the ends of the earth'! And you might as well at once give up any hope of attaching any numerical values of time or space to this series of indications. How many times, at the end of a hard day's trudging through the wearisome bush, utterly worn out, I have asked:

'Still far away?'

'Wapi, Bwana, iko karibu. No fear, Master, nearby.'

After which we walked on for more than an hour . . .

Somewhere, then, there was a village that was 'karibu kidogo'. Richard tried to persuade the medical orderly to send someone to recruit three men.

'I have nobody, Master. They all sick.'

It was clearly out of the question for him to go himself: he was much too advanced for jobs of that sort. By keeping on at the subject we got him to send a little boy in the end. Some hours later the boy came back alone. We have never known what was the cause of our not getting porters —whether excess of dignity, lack of good will, indolence, indifference, or what. In the end Richard got the urchin himself to act as our guide to the lake. Had he ever gone to the little village or not? Anyway, he also refused to carry anything, so we had to do without the tent and any sort of indulgence in the way of foodstuffs. Richard's own boy loaded himself up with the light camp-beds, drinks, and a hurricane-lamp. And we took our sleeping-bags, instruments, and food.

Now that we were progressing on foot we felt much closer to the country: it is astounding to what extent a vehicle cuts you off from nature. A first hill was quickly climbed. From the top of it Richard pointed out two parallel peaks, somewhat higher. The lake must be behind the second of them. After coming down the other side and crossing a series of dense thickets, we found ourselves climbing a steep incline. The horse-flies were stinging hard. Our sulky little guide would not speak a word. Sometimes he vanished from sight, then reappearing, light, slim and black in his tiny loin-cloth, always clasping his spear.

I began to feel tired. The last climb seemed very long. The countryside was so dry that it became steadily more monotonous. But towards the top the incline decreased, and then there we suddenly were, over the hill. Then came a stretch of level ground where umbelled acacias unfortunately impeded our view. Suddenly we found ourselves, to our surprise, on the edge of a rapid decline. Before us was a vast expanse of dark water, on the opposite bank of which the immense cliffs of the Rift towered high. But it was only in the northern half of the lake that the water was dark. In the south it was tinged an incredible rose-pink, a pure, satiny, luminous pink of fairy-tale delicacy. Birds! Flamingos!—tens of thousands of flamingos huddling close together on the water . . .

A wide flat bank ran along this edge of the lake. We hurried down, leaving the boy and the packages at the foot of the hill, near a rock that would do to mark the site of our camp. On the spongy ground there were large quantities of thin, brittle bones, and feathers too, some of them quite fresh, most of them withered and brown— decaying remains of slaughtered birds, and guano . . . As we drew nearer we crouched down and went forward cautiously. I had a colour-film in my Rolleiflex and was longing to get close enough to take some photographs of that rose-pink—which in its way would be as sensational as the crimson of molten lava. But suddenly a great din arose, a sudden chattering, a sound like a storm-wind, and thousands and thousands of scared birds went wheeling up into the air. For several minutes the sky was filled with the beating of their wings. Then, reassured by our re-maining quite still, they gradually settled again, in astonishingly regular lines. A second, and then a third attempt were both as vain as the first. Giving up any hope of stalking them, we went off to look for the hot springs.

At least a dozen of them gushed up at various points along the shore. In spite of the high temperature of the air in the sunlight, a light plume of white steam floated above each of them. Armed with a whole series of thermometers, Richard took temperatures, which were invariably that of boiling water at this altitude of several thousand feet: namely ninety-three, ninety-five, ninety-four . . . Being very rich in minerals, these waters all left heavy incrustations. Some of them had formed beautiful basins rising tier upon tier around a common centre; others spurted up through real pipes they had themselves formed; and yet others, less rich in precipitable salts, had contented themselves with building up a series of steps down which the hot water cascaded, singing. Around each of the springs lay the scalded corpses of unwary flamingos, slender bones, feathers caught by the steam. The clear, boiling water brimmed over in some places out of sandy basins, in others out of lovely bowls of bright stone, and ran in swift streamlets down into the lake.

Clumps of short reeds grew on this part of the vast strand. On several occasions I tried to crawl through these reeds in order to get closer to the waders. But it was no good.

In some places the ground was covered with curious heaps of earth in the shape of a fez or an upturned bucket, the uppermost surface having a slight dent in it. These were nests—they were the nests on which, when the season came, the female flamingos would lay and hatch their eggs.

Night fell swiftly, as it always does in that part of the world.

We ate our meal and talked, sitting round a blazing fire. Richard was particularly interested in the hot springs, belated manifestations, as they were, of volcanic activity. He was making a comparative study of the temperatures, the composition of the solvent salts, and the geological situation of various mineral irruptions that he had come

across in the course of his wanderings. The percentage of
mineral salts and the nature of these salts depends partly
on the kind of terrain the water flows through on its long
subterranean journeys and partly on the composition of
the 'juvenile' emanations, that is to say, of the emanations
from the magma, which enrich the water in which they are
diluted.

Generally speaking, the water is of atmospheric origin.
When the ground below it is very porous (lava, for instance),
full of cracks, or, as also occurs, easily soluble, the water
can go down to a very great depth. Sometimes when
following some inclined stratum it comes under other
strata that, being impenetrable, then hold it prisoner.
The slowness with which water moves underground pro-
longs its contact with the rocks, and this long contact,
combined with the particularly high temperature of the
volcanic substances some distance under the surface, en-
courages the solution of the minerals, which are silica,
carbonates of lime or magnesium, alkaline salts, and also
chlorides, sulphides, ammonium salts, fluorine salts and
others, contained in the deposits from the volcanic vapours.

Apart from water of atmospheric origin, it is possible,
even indeed probable, that juvenile water-vapour, escaping
as a result of the differentiation of the magma, rich in
salts and dilute gases from the same source, also comes
down to these deep layers and become enriched.

The time comes when these waters manage to return to
the surface of the earth. Either for reasons of a topographical
nature, or as a result of the geological texture of the rocks
above them, or again under the pressure of volcanic gases,
they finally gush up in the form of mineral springs. When
they are very hot, like those we had here, or like the one
I had found a short time before at Katanga, they are
generally richer in salts than cooler springs are, and hence
also have an increased tendency to form incrustations.[1] All

---

[1] On the other hand, certain cool springs that are very rich in easily soluble
and precipitable carbonates also have this property of forming thick incrustations.

this explains why hot springs are often found to be of a volcanic nature, as are for instance those of Vichy, La Bourboule, and Mont-Dore, which are in the same district as the cinder-cones of Auvergne, and likewise Spa, on the fringe of the former volcanic region of the Eiffel, Solfatara (where the Romans themselves went to 'take the waters') in the volcanic area of Naples, and so on.

MEMORIES OF JAVA

I had told Richard about our climb down into Niragongo. That evening it was his turn. He spent the evening hours describing to me another descent, one that had succeeded only after several abortive attempts and, in spite of considerable difficulties; it was in the remote and mysterious land of Java.

The *caldera* of Mount Raoung was another that was reputed to be inaccessible. It is one of the most famous eruptive centres of that large island known as 'the island of volcanoes', and its terrible reputation was the first obstacle the volcanologist came up against. But it was not the only one. Before the summit could be reached, there were two days of solid hacking away through the jungle. And then came the descent itself, the most difficult part of all. Standing on the edge of the abyss, a thousand feet deep or more, Richard felt himself irresistibly drawn to it. At the centre of the enormous cauldron he could see the huge swelling of an inner cone, its open maw ceaselessly spewing forth a column of grey-white vapour.

'I couldn't *not* go down!' Richard said to me.

How well I knew what he meant!

The Malayan coolies, however, did not by any means feel the same attraction. The one thing which they found almost irresistible was the desire to scramble as fast as they could down the slopes they had just climbed up.

For the first attempt Richard had had a sort of wickerwork gondola brought up. When all the preparations had been made, he climbed into this, accompanied by a dog and some equipment. The dog's function was to warn him of the presence of carbonic oxide. This gas, which is heavier than air, tends to hang about in depressions, and has no smell. The dog, being nearer the ground than a man, would feel the effects sooner than himself and thus warn him of the danger. It was the classic method, which is still used in some of the caves in the Bay of Naples.

Fifteen coolies let the car down slowly by a long rope. At first all went well. By means of shouts and signals, Richard kept in touch with a man posted on the edge of the *caldera*. But after a while the 'gondola' struck an overhang. One corner of the basket settled there quite gently, while the rest began to tip gradually over into empty space as the men above continued paying out the rope. Richard barely had time to grab hold of the sides and stop himself from sliding right out. Then the bottom of the basket suddenly detached itself. After a leap out into space, it resumed its proper angle but then began spinning at the end of the rope, first in one direction, then in the other . . . From that moment communications between the explorer and his team were cut. Going on down and down, rather like a miserable spider at the end of its thread, frequently in jerks, and banged against the cliff wall, the basket and its cargo pursued their uncomfortable voyage. The man found the experience anything but pleasant, and the dog was beside itself with terror, crouched whining and howling at the bottom of the basket. This lasted till the whole of the rope had been paid out. They had descended over six hundred feet, taking almost an hour. Then Richard realised that he had come only half way. For lack of guide marks he had underestimated the depth of the precipice. The ascent was in keeping with the descent: bumps, sudden stops, and wild surges upward under the vigorous tugging of fifteen men in a great hurry to have done with the job.

Some months later Raoung began to erupt. Richard heard it from his plantation forty miles away. During the first minutes he thought it was a distant storm. But the persistence of the deep rumbling, with the sharper crackling of explosions on top of it, soon convinced him that it was really a reawakening of the volcano.

And then, some hours later, very fine white ash began to rain down. They got into one's eyes and gritted between the teeth . . . The usual day's rain came down in the form of drops of mud. 'I was driving the car when the rain began to come down, in that violent way you know for yourself,' Richard told me. 'The wind-screen was opaque in a moment; I was absolutely blinded. You can imagine how I stood on the brakes!'

When he was able to get to the scene, only a few days later, in the company of one of the geologists of the volcanological service, the eruption had decreased in intensity, and the two men were able to reach the edge of the *caldera* without danger. In the cauldron itself, the central peak, which on Richard's previous visit had been so placid, had a red, grumbling mouth wide open to the sky, and surging out of it, with deafening uproar, came 'packets' of dense grey and black smoke and bursts of incandescent bombs.

'It was like some kind of dark brain developing very fast. The feeling you get of a budding, "active", living brain is quite extraordinary,' said Richard, who does not happen to be the sort of man that is easily amazed. The big bombs, he told me, rose hundreds of feet. 'They generally fell on the sides of the peak, but they also landed all over the bottom of the cauldron. The noise was so deafening that we couldn't hear each other speak.'

'How about the lava flows?'

'There weren't any. Too viscous, I suppose. It all came out in the shape of bombs and ashes.'

Two years passed. The volcano became completely dormant, and the people at the observatories gave their assurance that there was not the slightest danger of an imminent eruption. Richard thought it was a good opportunity to return to the attack.

His previous experience had made him decide firmly against the basket method. So he replaced it by a simple

system of webbing. He had a telephone-cable passed
through the interior of his safety-rope. With earphones over
his head and a speaking-tube fixed in front of his mouth,
he began by thinking it was all wonderful. He could com-
municate with the team up aloft, directing manœuvres in
such a way that the descent was correctly conducted. But
the greater the distance became, the greater was the
increase in the elasticity of the rope. Richard soon had the
disagreeable feeling that he was dangling at the end of a
long spring. Finally he heard a crackling in his head-
phones. 'Hello! Hello! Hello!' There was no answer to
his calls. The metal telephone cable had been stretched
till it could stand the strain no longer, and had that
moment snapped. He could not go on like this! Thus at
eight hundred feet down, this time, the second attempt
was also defeated by an unforeseen difficulty.

A year later, in 1932, a camp was once again set up
on the top of the mountain. This time Richard brought a
large team of coolies with him and at once set about having
a winding stairway constructed down the steep slope (with
its angle of 60 degrees), leading right to the bottom. It
was made of steel eye-bolts sunk into the narrow fissures in
the hard rock of the old outflows, steps hacked out of the
mighty strata of tuff with the pick-axe, rope-ladders fixed
into the rock as a way over overhangs, rope ramps, wire
ramps, wooden rungs . . . It was a week's hard work,
and he had all the time to keep on exhorting the men to
carry on with the job they had begun, to prevent desertions
by natives terrified of the precipice, the smoke, the clattering falls of stones, the devils, the gods, the mists, and
everything . . . He had to encourage them by word and
by example, to distribute rum, to be gentle and persuasive
and at the same time sharply authoritative. With every
inch the 'path' got nearer to the bottom, the greater the
coolies' subdued terror became, and work went forward

only to the accompaniment of an incessant murmur of litanies . . .

It should be said that Java, which has a hundred and twenty-five volcanoes, several of which are in more or less continual eruption, has been the scene of cataclysms violent and horrible beyond anything known elsewhere in the world. In 1822, for instance, Galung-Gung, which was believed to be extinct, buried villages, human beings and cattle under a blanket of blue mud several yards thick.[1] On that occasion there were more than 4,000 dead. Keluit killed 5,500 persons in 1919. Papandayan killed 3,000 in 1772, Merapi 1,300 in 1931, Krakatoa 36,000 in 1883, Tomboro 12,000 in 1815, when only 26 human beings in the whole province escaped alive. So it is quite understandable that the Javanese villagers, knowing the long and hard tradition of their 'tutelary' volcanoes, were not over-eager to accompany Richard on his explorations.

Nevertheless, what he was trying to do was far from foolhardy. There is nothing rash or wild about my friend Richard! When he decided to go down into this gulf full of smoke and gas, he knew, as I have said, that the seismographs, clinometers, thermographs and so forth had all certified that there was no danger of an eruption. After a week's toil, his goal was achieved. For the first time man had set foot on the bottom of Gounoung Raung.

Richard pitched two tents there, one for himself, the other for the three Malays whom he had talked into staying with him. They had also succeeded in bringing down material and provisions, but the problem was a water-supply. It had been decided that a couple of coolies would

[1] The volcanic character of these regions, as we have already seen, is very different from what is found in the *interior* of continents or oceans. The acidity and viscosity of their lava is what makes for the different character of these 'fringe' volcanoes, causing them to be extremely violent in their explosiveness. Their paroxysms cause terrible destruction, partly as a result of the showers of thousands of tons of rock and ash flung out, partly because of the avalanches of hot mud they set moving. These avalanches are sometimes due to the fact that water-courses are almost instantaneously choked up by hot ashes, but sometimes also to the presence of a peaceful lake at the bottom of the crater in a dormant volcano, the waters of which are then flung out to a great distance.

bring it each day from the first spring found on the outer slopes of the volcano. But after having once brought half-empty cans, the team deserted, terrified by the long solitary journey. So the four men remained isolated at the bottom of the cauldron.

Richard's intention was to make a precise topographical survey of the crater, locate all the volcanic fumes, and note the temperature of each of them. Apart from this long-term job, he wanted to get as complete as possible a collection of specimens of rock. But by the end of the second day the situation was already critical. The last drop of water had been drunk. On the third day the Malay consented to drink tinned milk—they would never so much as sip fresh milk, which is only for babies to drink!

At the end of that day one of the natives fled. About eight o'clock that evening the men sitting near the tents at the bottom of the crater suddenly heard long wails of distress from up above—from very far above their heads: it was the miserable coolie, who had gone off too late and been overtaken by darkness somewhere on the cliffs. Panic-stricken, all alone in the hostile immensity of the place, he kept hailing his comrades in order to comfort himself with the sound of the human voice. All that night long plaintive cries were exchanged in that infernal cauldron, echoing back from the rock-walls.

In order to forestall any fresh desertion, Richard, who wanted to hold out another twenty-four hours in order to take at least the principal temperatures,[1] ordered his men to keep together. However, thirst was becoming intolerable. Although respiration was not interfered with by the gases, the gases were having other destructive effects: after those three days the canvas of the tents tore across like blotting-paper. I don't know who was most impressed, Richard who knew the reason for it, or the natives who attributed it to local devils and did all their jobs muttering prayers.

[1] A map of the bottom of the *caldera* showed more than a hundred vents of volcanic fumes. The following year differences in temperature could be observed. The temperature of vent No. 79, for instance, had risen from 109 degrees in 1931 to 159 degrees centigrade.

They had been all over the enormous cauldron in the persistent hope of discovering some pool left over since the last rains. It had all petered away in that ashy ground, which was porous as sand. With equal lack of success they scoured the six or seven thousand yards of the circumference: there was not the slightest moisture trickling out of the foot of those vertiginous walls.[1]

Desperate at the prospect of having to abandon the work half done, Richard scanned his kingdom of seven or eight hundred acres. 'Over there, at the other end?' he wondered. 'Perhaps.' He had caught sight of the remains of a small interior cone similar to that in the middle of the crater. That ancient pile must have had plenty of time to cool off, and the inclination of the strata seemed favourable. Once more they went right across the scarred floor of the crater, stumbling in the outflows, plunging deep into ashes. Now they were slowly going round this old fragment of a cone. Suddenly, at the foot of the little mound they saw a tiny trickle of water oozing out, like a piece of dark string on the volcanic dust. Avidly, one after the other, they put their lips to it. By slightly hollowing out the friable rock they then succeeded in forming a trap-system that gave them up to a gallon a day.

The work of the survey continued. It was arduous. The nights were cold. In order to get warm the men scratched away the crust that had formed on the surface of ashes they were lying on, and then the humid heat of the volcanic vapours filled the tent.

When they at last returned to the top of the mountain, they found that the corrosive action of the gases was such that it had *reduced by half* the diameter of the thick wire cable that had served as a ramp along the steep path down the cliff. Soon nothing would be left of all that labour but a little rust and some thin scraps of rope eaten away by acids . . .

[1] And for a good reason: these walls were the result of an explosion or of the blowing off, all in one piece, of the central part of the original cone, which had been formed by the accumulation of strata of lava outflows and tuff. All these strata 'hung' towards the exterior, parallel with the external slopes of the volcano, and the rain-water that infiltrated them naturally disappeared.

It was no longer of any consequence, however, for henceforth Raung counted among the volcanoes which had been studied, if not actually tamed. Now it was known how to make the descent in order to continue the study of the fumes and of the variations in temperature. A new step had been taken in the forecasting of eruptions.

While Richard was recounting these reminiscences, whole squadrons of mosquitoes were zooming round our heads, attracted by our fire. In the end we could stand them no more and, having warmed up, we took the hurricane-lamp and returned to the shore. It was two hundred paces or so away from the camp. From the lake we could hear the quiet, vague sound of colonies of flamingos, rather like some immense, far-away cooing of ring-doves.

Now we found no difficulty in getting much closer to the birds than we had been able to by day. In the clear night we could see them huddled close together, suddenly all moving off in the same direction, then swerving away in another direction, and then in a third . . . Sometimes they stayed motionless for several minutes, and then, at a soundless command from some invisible general, the whole army resumed its slow, perfect, silent manœuvres.

We got to within ten yards of them. Then all of a sudden the rank closest to us rose into the air with a tremendous beating of wings; then the second rose in the same way; and the movement, spreading out like a wave, finally reached the furthermost lines. In a minute or two the dark sky overhead seemed filled with the eddying of beating wings. But almost at once the vanguard had settled again, only a little further away, followed by the rest of the army flying down and settling too.

Creeping along the shore, we came on other assemblies of birds, and each time their reaction was exactly the same. Nevertheless, as we walked on, having lit our lamp again, suddenly, as we were drawing near to yet another colony on the ground, one of the birds detached itself from the main body and went straight for our lamp. Advancing at some speed on its long slender knock-kneed legs, it came and thrust its head against the metal guard of the lantern, staggered, and then doggedly made another onslaught. I tried to catch hold of it by the body, but it escaped and then returned to make another dash at the lamp, which Richard was holding out at arm's length. It fell back two or three paces, hesitantly, and then came on again at our light, like a drunk man. I grabbed it, seizing its long supple neck with both hands and then stopped the furious beating of its wings by holding them close to its body, so that I managed to tuck the bird under my arm.

I was slightly astonished at its size, which I had imagined to be greater. It is true that the pictures I had been shown never showed any points of reference. These flamingos are in fact no bigger than a goose, but their legs are about eighteen inches long. The long and flexible neck is not as strong as that of a swan, and the head ends in a thick, inelegant beak of disproportionate size. Why did this one come and fling itself at our lantern like that, behaving so differently from his more disciplined fellows? After having taken some specimens of its beautiful pink feathers, we set it free again.

The rest of our night on the edge of the lake was spent in defensive operations—keeping on the move all the time —against the buzzing clouds of mosquitoes.

The next day Richard thought we would travel a good few miles in a northerly direction and reach Lake Baringo, where there are important native fisheries; it is connected with civilisation by a motor-road. So we returned to our car. Zigzagging along, stopped now by the cone of one of the numerous volcanoes in that immense valley, now by one of its infrequent rivers, we kept on trying to make headway towards the north. We had to make up

our minds to cross the fairly wide stream that we had
come up against various times and kept trying to get
round. In order to prevent the motor-car from sinking
up to the axles in the mud on the banks, I set out on foot
to reconnoitre our way across. Arriving at the brink, I
was put to flight by a saurian of what seemed to be a
pretty fair size, but which however also seemed to me to
be longer-legged and to stand higher than a crocodile and
to be endowed with an agility on solid ground that was
extremely surprising to me. I saw it running over the
shingle very fast, putting down its paws rather in the same
way as a dog running. It dived in and disappeared. When
I described it to Richard, he said he thought it must be
a kind of iguana.

I then crossed the stream, which was about thirty yards
wide, and having established the fact that the water nowhere came higher than my knees, I reported back to
Richard and he drove the car across.

After that we wandered through a dry, scorched world
that was almost all sheer desert. In the end, however, we
came upon a village, which at first seemed to be empty.
But our luck had turned: the first native who appeared
on the scene could speak Swahili. Further, he was quite
delighted with the suggestion that he should get into the
motor-car and act as guide to us. Thanks to him we henceforth made good progress through the level districts,
avoiding the volcanic structures and impassable canyons.

All went perfectly till the moment when we had a fresh
watercourse to cope with, this one not as wide as the last,
but with pretty steep banks. Richard drove down very
carefully and very slowly, then accelerated as much as
possible in the stream itself, successfully reached the further
bank, which rose at an angle of thirty degrees, drove about
a length up it, skidded in the gluey clay—and slid backwards until the driving-wheels once again got a hold on
the pebbles of the river-bed.

After that it went on for hours—I don't know how many
hours—in which we used every means to hand, every

means that our bush-dwellers' ingenuity inspired us with, and gained height inch by inch. Ropes, pulling, pushing, building up the clay ground with a covering of pebbles, clearing away all the boulders that formed over-large impediments in the way of the wheels, making various kinds of use of the two jacks there were in the boot, letting the engine turn slowly in order to gain a few inches surreptitiously, racing the motor in an attempt to take the bank by storm . . . we tried it all. I can see myself now, with my clayey hands trying to keep steady the one jack thanks to which we had raised the back of the car, while the two Negroes were piling up pebbles and brushwood under it. But the ground on which the jack was standing kept slipping and slipping and in spite of all my efforts the jack suddenly toppled over. The car gave the back of my hand a blow that put it fairly completely out of action for more than a fortnight.

Still, we did get out of it in the end. A few miles further on we reached a village on the edge of a watercourse that this time turned out to be impassable. We had reached the road from Nakuru to Lake Baringo. The primitive bridge across the river had been swept away some time earlier and a Hindu foreman was superintending the building of a permanent stone bridge. He told us that lorries went across, pushed by hand, with the engine wrapped in sacks. After hesitating for a long time, weighing the pros and cons, being afraid that our engine, which was of course much nearer the ground than a lorry engine, might be flooded and so keep us there for several days, we had to give up our hope of reaching Lake Baringo this time.

CHAPTER XVI

RETURN TO EUROPE: STROMBOLI

I WAS not destined to see Lake Baringo. The time was drawing near for me to embark at Mombasa, and I had to leave my friends and that pleasant country, Kenya.

In two days I crossed the terrain separating me from the Indian Ocean. It is one of the parts of the world most amazingly rich in game, with hundreds upon hundreds of antelopes, from those ugly and ungraceful gnus to the elegant kobs, with I don't know how many other species in between. There were companies of ostriches, looking highly disdainful, with extraordinary thick, strong legs. There were lions, wonderfully tranquil and lithe, and troops of zebras, plump, jolly-looking creatures, which I had heard a five-year-old child at Katanga refer to as 'donkeys in pyjamas'. And then there were those strange animals that seem to have come straight out of the secondary era —the giraffes, which are at once ridiculous and somehow lovable.

My boat was delayed, and I had forty-eight hours to hang about on the edge of that immense sea. Bright sandy beaches, nestling below banks on which the airy coconut palms stand high, line the slack-water lagoon that is separated from the open sea by a single line of coral reefs.

Then there were days after days on the purple water of the ocean. We rounded the reddish cliffs of Ras Hafun,

at the extreme tip of Samalia, and dropped anchor in the
roads at Aden.

This ancient Arab city has what is, I believe, the unique
peculiarity of having been built at the bottom of an extinct
crater. The *caldera* is two or three miles across and its
walls in places rise three hundred to a thousand feet.
The only way into the interior of this colossal fortress is
through a narrow gap that had to be blown into the walls
by dynamite in order to bring the modern road through.

It is already five thousand years since man constructed
vast stone reservoirs that even now bear hardly any traces
of age. Those great workers of damage by erosion, trickling
water and frost, are non-existent here. And the terrible
desert wind, which wears everything away under the
grinding of the sand, cannot penetrate inside this gigantic
rampart.

The ship sailed on, and all through the Red Sea we
caught sight of beautiful arid desert islands, volcanic cones
strung out in straight lines, all along the parallel faults
that gash the bottom of this legendary sea.[1]

A week later we were told that we should be passing
Stromboli about dawn next morning. I was up on deck
while it was still dark, for fear of missing it. We were
sailing along the Sicilian coast, which was dotted with
thousands of little twinkling lights. Villages and little
towns, street lamps, lighted windows—all made these
shores seem to be vibrating and smiling at us. It was my
first glimpse of Europe after years in Africa. Dawn was
just breaking as we passed Messina. Scylla and Charybdis,
seen from the deck of a large modern steamer, seemed so
insignificant that it was quite disappointing; but soon we
saw ahead, gradually emerging from the early morning
haze, the conic island that was Stromboli.

It seemed to be coming closer and growing larger. The

[1] It is known that these fractures were caused by the old continent's splitting
apart: Africa pulled towards the West, Arabia towards the East. The water
of the ocean invaded this colossal rent in the crust of the earth, and the deep
magma gushed to the surface. In this way the old Aden volcano was born,
and likewise those in the Red Sea, in Arabia, and in Africa.

sunlight touched its summit, and then in a few moments poured over the whole island. There was a low belt of sparse vegetation, and a group of white houses clustered close to the sea, looking terribly forlorn and cut off from the rest of the world. All the rest, which was practically the whole of this mountain looming straight up out of the wine-dark sea, was scarps of brown rock, steep black cliffs, reddish overhangs. Over the peak itself a plume of smoke drifted, floating out sideways.

The ship was swiftly coming up round the southern side of the volcano. Here was level ground, no trace of green vegetation or of any life at all. The gloomy rock plunged straight down into the sea. We were leaving the mountain behind to starboard. Its western flank was nothing but a colossal slope of scoriae and crumbling falls of stone broken away from the cliffs, a steady drop running straight down from the vapour-laden crater to the flashing water. Sailing past here in the night, one of the sailors told me, they sometimes saw bright red flows trickling down that slope and into the sea.

The island was already growing smaller in the thinning mists. The volcano looked as though it were sunk in deep sleep. For a long time I stood gazing back, with longing in my heart, at that triangle gradually growing fainter in the distance. So that was the fabulous island of Stromboli, one of the most famous volcanoes in the world.

I did not think I would see it again so soon. However, it was only six months later that I disembarked there.

I was both delighted and disappointed. I was delighted to get to know this champion of volcanic regularity at last. And I was disappointed because . . .

The newspapers had announced, in screaming headlines, that an 'extremely violent' eruption was going on. I took a plane and landed at Naples. At Naples, in that immense, swarming, idle city, nobody seemed to care in the least about Stromboli. Perhaps, I said to myself, having Lord Vesuvius so near makes the Neapolitans a little insensitive to whatever may be happening in the islands of Lipari. Still, my confidence had suffered its first blow.

The flight from Brussels to Naples had taken us only four hours, in spite of having to cross the Alps. From Naples onward, even though Stromboli was hardly a hundred miles away as the crow flies, I soon found one had to begin counting in aeons.

There was a wait . . . Then a train . . . Then a wait at Reggio . . . Then a ferry-boat. A wait at Messina . . . A little local railway as far as the little port of Milazzo . . . Yet another wait . . . Then a boat . . . Ages passed, in the course of which we learned that Stromboli was indeed in eruption, *ma, insomma, non tanto terribile.* And in the ages our journey took there was only one thought that haunted us: would we arrive in time to see anything at all?

How maddening if I should be unable to show Picciotto anything but a bit of smoke!

Picciotto was an Italian friend of mine, whom I had torn away from his laboratory in Brussels by sheer force of describing to him the splendour of incandescent lava. I was nervous of the expression in the physicist's sparkling, slightly teasing green eyes . . . Was the volcanologist not in danger of losing face? Another let-down for me after being swept away once again by my natural tendency to over-enthusiasm!

As it went on its quiet way, our *piroscafo*—a vessel painted white—touched at one after another of those little Aeolian islands, all of them volcanic, that dot the wonderful blue of the Tyrrhenian Sea. First of all there is Vulcano, which gets its name from the god of the subterranean forges and has become as it were godfather to all the volcanoes on earth. It has been dormant now for sixty years, in that deceptive sleep that often precedes the rudest awakenings. It is a smoothly rising mountain thirteen hundred feet high, linked by a low isthmus to its younger brother Vulcanello; its general colour is a pleasant grey that is easy on the eye, gashed by the rusty red of the ferrous oxides and the yellow of sulphur. White vapours (sulphur dioxide, sulphuretted hydrogen and water-vapour) are exhaled here and there, even through the bottom of the sea several cable-lengths from the shore, making the blue water boil and bubble and gurgle alarmingly.

One hour's walking brings us to the peak, which opens into a wide regular basin furrowed by avalanches of dry dust and going down to a small flat door at the centre, a thousand feet down below.

Like Lipari, its extinct and eroded neighbour, Vulcano is a volcano that produces lava of the most viscous type, which is also the most acid.[1] Hence the eruptions are terrible. But instead of shooting out laterally in 'burning clouds' as happened in the case of Mont Pelée, the gases are ejected vertically, to a very great height, together with the millions of tons of lava that they pulverise. A dark column shoots thousands of feet straight up into the air and spreads out like a black mushroom, jagged by lightning-flashes, out of which the bombs rain down; and this mushroom goes on swelling and expanding like an enormous sooty cauliflower. Vulcano's last eruption began in 1888. It lasted two years. The scanty farms were ravaged, and the houses of the few islanders, who were either fishermen or sulphur quarriers, were destroyed. These people came back afterwards, and built new houses and sowed fresh crops. . .

At the next island, Lipari, one is in the realm of *pumice*. Pumice-stone is one of the acid varieties of lava. Chemically it is almost pure glass, riddled by myriads of little holes, the hollows left by the gas bubbles in what was once a thick paste. There are so incredibly many of these little cavities that the apparent density[2] of pumice is less than that of water. So it happens that after eruptions of

[1] These are the rhyolites and their associates, all very rich in silica, and silicic oxide, the crystalline form of which is quartz and the amorphous vitreous form, glass.

[2] That of the rock *and* of the cavities, the *real* density being that of the compact rock alone.

this pattern the sea is often found to be covered with porous lava floating on the waves, sometimes over vast areas. When one sees Lipari, that light-coloured mountain of pumice-stone, rising out of the blue distances, one's first disconcerting impression is of a snowy peak under the almost African dark blue of the sky. The white quarries are torrid under the blazing sun. Half-naked, brown as Bedouins, the thin, muscular men who work there toil at hacking out the dazzling stone that thunderous crushing-machines then grind to fragments, or to powder, and the blinding dust overlays everything, blurs every trace of colour and mercilessly dries the throat.

There is a breach in the 'snow-mountain' towards the north-east. These enormous indentations that sometimes jag craters of this type are known as *barrancos*. Creeping out cf the barranco, like some great dark green alligator, is an enormous flow of obsidian, its lustre so dark as to be almost black, that makes its ponderous way down into the sea.

After the twin nipples of Salina, which the Greeks compared to the perfect breasts of a virgin goddess, come bare cliffs: this is Panaria, a cluster of light-coloured donjons rising out of the sea, the remains of an ancient volcano that destroyed itself in its last explosion.

At last, several miles ahead, we see the dark triangle of Stromboli rising from the sea!

I stare at it for all I am worth. Beside me, equally intent, are my friend Picciotto and Professor Faraone, who has been with us since leaving Messina. Whatever we have been told, we have gone on hoping all the time that we would still see over the peak that famous *pino*, that great umbrella of smoke and ashes showing that Stromboli is in explosive eruption. Alas, there was nothing more than a tuft of brown and rusty vapours to be seen, driven sideways by the wind from the north-west.

Seen from the sea the volcano appears to be conical; but it is in reality a pyramid with a rectangular base, the sides of which are about a mile long. Its peak is at a height of 2,940 feet. Its real foundations, furthermore, are more

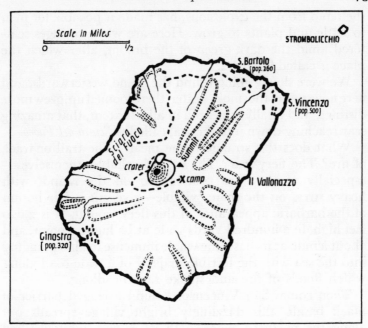

than 500 fathoms below sea-level, so that it is in fact ten times the size of Vesuvius, whose approximately three thousand feet rest on the ground of the Italian peninsula.

Like the whole eastern part of the island, Stromboli's summit belongs to an ancestor of the present volcano. One day a terrific explosion shattered the earlier mountain, and in the enormous rent opened in its western side a new Stromboli later developed, welded together, as it were, with the old one that had produced it. The character of the lava changed. Instead of the relatively acid *andesites* that the first volcano had emitted, it was now fluid basalt that came pouring out.

The boat was coming up to the south of the island. Here were congealed lava flows, overhangs, enormous machicolations, and vertical cliffs of black rock. A wall of rock here dropped sheer to the sea. This coast was not merely uninviting; it was inaccessible.

It is at the south-western tip that an area of flat ground,

sheltered from the explosions, has made it possible for men to settle and plants to grow. Here are white cottages scattered amid the dark green of the broom, after which the place is called Ginostra.

We were slowly going round the island westerwards, and here now, under the smoky crater, there loomed up, grew more distinct, and finally appeared in all its extent, that amazing scar reaching down into the sea, called *la Sciara del Fuoco*.

What does this strange name mean? The trail or track of fire? The fiery scar? The rugged syllables themselves—especially as they are pronounced on the island, with heavy stress on the main syllable—give one a fair notion of the barbaric appearance of this fiery wound. It is 2,620 feet high, five hundred yards wide at its highest point, and about a mile at its base, the whole immense incline plunging into the sea with the terrible majesty of a wide road along which floods of fire and smoke race headlong.

Then comes San Vincenzo. Behind a jagged barrier of black basalt, this dazzlingly bright village spreads out along the northern shore, with its square, white-washed houses and its narrow little streets winding between the flowery gardens. The place seems asleep, wrapped in a silence that is hardly ruffled—at least for the moment—by the roar of the surf and the whisper of the breeze among the olive-trees. Some acres of poor corn, some vineyards clinging to the side of the mountain, ten olive-groves, and some capers with their strange mauve flowers and magical scent, some fishing-boats drawn up on the beach —that is all these people have or need. They labour on the soil or on the sea, making a poor living, but in peace. They make the most of some decades of calm between two violent eruptions.

We have pitched our tent at an altitude of nearly three thousand feet, in a valley of black scoriae separated from the great crater itself by the shoulder of the peak.

Out of this gloomy basalt slag, these hailstones that have accumulated here in the course of successive eruptions, rise the rusty age-old towers of andesite that are the remains of the original volcano.

We do some preliminary reconnoitring.

We explore the edges of the summit, the southern lip of the deep basin, at the bottom of which we can see the enormous vertical shaft of the chimney itself. The steep slopes falling away under our feet to the very edge of that gaping maw do not exist on the other side of the shaft: there the side of the chimney rises straight up to a narrow ridge separating it from the Sciara del Fuoco.

Pit—as Picciotto is called—has adjusted his helmet. Clad in khaki shirt and shorts, he is a mere bright speck among all this rubble as he begins to climb down into the crater. The loose scree rolls away under his feet, bouncing, finally vanishing among the vapours from the abyss. He risks going as far as the great fissures that run concentrically round the lips of the chimney down below. But his audacity is not rewarded. He has to climb up again without having been able to see through the opaque screen of fumes.

Measurements taken on the edge of the crater by means of an ionisation chamber show the local radio-activity to be practically nil.[1] Faraone, who, like Picciotto, is a physicist, and who has come here specifically to take these measurements, is considerably disappointed. Thirst, fatigue, and the implacable glare of the sun are gradually getting the better of our muscles and our brains. Professor Faraone goes down to the village again, accompanied by the two young islanders who have acted as guides to us. They

---

[1] At Vulcano the radio-activity in the atmosphere turned out to be very considerable. To what is the difference to be attributed? Perhaps to the nature of the lava: there it consisted of acidic rhyolites, which, like the granites, are very rich in radio-elements; here the lava consists of basalt, which contains almost none.

return the next day bringing us fresh supplies of bread and water.

Left alone in that strangely limited desert of ashes enveloped by the blue immensity of dazzling sky and sea, Pit and I search in vain for some scrap of shade. The sunlight casts its glare everywhere, and the interior of the tent is stifling.

Never before, not even in the heart of Africa, have I experienced the like of it. In the end we tilt the camp-bed up on end to form a sort of awning. We lie down close to it, getting at least our head and shoulders to some extent shaded from that frightful glare.

Towards the end of the afternoon, the burning heat decreases slightly and we return to the edge of the crater. Following the crest, we come to a sort of fault, the side of which is easy to climb. From the top we can look down into the abyss. A gust of wind clears the fumes away from the entry to it for about a minute and we are able to see that not many feet down the vertical walls become red and then, as the veil of gases covers them again, purplish crimson, as though they were poisonous.

'There you are, Pit, that's where we ought to have ourselves let down by a cable. Metal cable, of course. And in a fire-proof cage.'

With a short laugh, Picciotto shakes his curly head. His piercing eyes do not move from the abyss. And it is almost at once that he murmurs, quite seriously: 'There must be a way of doing it . . .'

So then I realise that in showing him Stromboli, the volcanologist has not lost face: for the physicist is now 'bitten' too.

From the height where our observatory was, which the islanders call Torrione di Ponente (The Tower of the Setting Sun), we were soon able to make sure that the torrents of lava that could be seen from out at sea, trickling down the Sciara del Fuoco, did not originate in the large crater. Here there was nothing to be seen that could be their source. On the other hand, beyond the deep vent we were now overlooking, there were two smaller orifices, which were vigorously spitting out dense whirls of white vapour. These gases, fumes, and vapours some distance up joined together with the exhalations from the principal chimney, forming a tremendous cloud that the south-westerly wind seized hold of and blew away.

There was something fascinating in the sight of these dense swirls being ceaselessly scattered, ceaselessly re-forming, and every now and then suddenly, for an instant, laying bare the glowing mouth of the chimney itself. Sometimes an unexpected growl would startle the flock of vapours, and red clots would be sent flying up towards the smoky, misty roof.

For a short while we considered *crossing* il Torrione, that is to say, going down the other side of it. It was a sheer cliff. Should we fix up a system of ropes? On reflection, it did not seem worth the amount of trouble involved. There must be some way of reaching the very lip of the chimney if one went some distance back. By following the solid lip that lay between the central shaft and the precipitous sides of la Sciara, it must be possible to reach the two secondary orifices that we could see from here. Perhaps we would even discover, somewhere over there, the origins of the torrents whose mysterious incandescence is the first sign of the island's presence that sailors see at night . . . If Stromboli had not had in store for us the grand spectacle we had rather thoughtlessly been led to expect by the newspaper reports, at least we were beginning to realise that this volcano had a secret after all and that it would be very interesting indeed to set out in search of the answer.

We spent the whole of the next day making topographical surveys, collecting specimens, and noting various observations of the volcano's behaviour. Above all we noted the frequency of the explosions, the *scoppi*, as the local people say, who hear them from their vineyards or in their beds. The 'bursts' were generally at intervals of twelve to fifteen minutes. That ought to give us time enough (we decided), after leaving the shelter of il Torrione, to cross the zone where the bombs fell and reach the area of the little vents before the next explosion.

TOWARDS THE SOURCES OF THE FIRE

The day after that, there was no more sun! The wind drove along before it a grey mist mingled with fumes. We went striding down our ravine and, nearly half a mile further on, having cut across to the right and crossed a secondary ridge and then another ravine, we reached the foot of il Torrione without encountering any difficulties. The incline was now acute. Each step sent pebbles rolling down into the depths, little clattering cascades that disappeared into the mist. The bare, solid rock of il Torrione, round the base of which we were going, served not merely as a shelter but also as a guide to us: by pressing the palms of our hands against it we could follow the base of the 'tower' without worrying overmuch about the scoriae rattling away under our feet as they were dislodged. Then we stopped, on the alert for the next *scoppio*.

'Prrrroup!' That was it.

We continued our journey almost at once. Crawling on all fours to save time, we scrambled up the seventy or eighty feet still between us and the rim of the shaft, and at last stood upright on the very lip of the abyss. On the right was the shaft of the main crater; on the left was the vast expanse of la Sciara. The narrow terrain on which we found ourselves was somewhat frightening. I preferred to make the return journey down the outer slope, even at the price of losing the advantage we had here of almost horizontal ground. We stumbled about for a long time in the moving masses of scoriae and debris.

We made a detour some way down in order to observe some enormous steaming crevasses. We crept along them with all possible care. A momentary rent in the screen of fumes revealed a sombre red glare, which was again instantly veiled from sight. Here were mazes of steep rocky walls, corridors of scoriae, narrow abysses. Sometimes a cluster of sulphur-yellow or orange crystals burst upon us, delighting our eyes. Then again came the sombre rusty bareness of the rocks, the dark brown and black we knew so well. A series of fractures cracking la Sciara and running right across our path forced us to climb back the way we had come. All at once, there was a *scoppio*. We were taken by surprise at the sound of it, a brief, hard growl. Instinctively we hunched our shoulders. The thought flashed through our minds: 'On a slope like this there's no chance of jumping to dodge anything.' But the explosion was already upon us and over—it had not come from the main crater, but from one of the two others, and the bombs would not fall here.

Faster, faster! Here was a vertical rock face: we worked round it. Here was a crevasse, a dead-end: we turned back and came out on a sort of vast terrace. We found ourselves walking along the surface of congealed lava, some corded, some more or less smooth. Some paces away, white puffs of steam shot up and eddied around, coming out of one of the two little orifices that we had seen from il Torrione. It was as though the steam were in a great hurry to escape from whatever was going on in the depths. Two paces away from one of these vents, which was five or six yards across, we were stopped by the heat. The pyroscope gave us a reading of nine hundred and eighty degrees centigrade. All the same, a look inside that would be something really worth while!

We explored the terrace, walking carefully. Here basaltic tumuli alternated with ditches, faults, avenues of black rock. Ah, here was a pool of solid lava! The dark, petrified ripples circled out from a faintly steaming hole in the centre, which was fringed with a thin edging, blindingly white. This pool must have been liquid only some days earlier. Then I caught sight of a hillock on the edge of the terrace, overlooking la Sciara. I scrambled up it. There was nothing to be seen—not a trace of live lava. On the other side was a fall of loose debris, beyond that long smooth slabs. Suddenly, through a sort of window opened

by the collapse of a slab of basalt, I found myself looking
straight into a dazzling, flashing tunnel. I could not help
exclaiming. In no time Pit had joined me. Our eager gaze
fastened, intent, on a strange river gliding along under the
arcade, swiftly and silently, a scarlet liquid running down
this slightly inclined tube. Our eyes followed it right down
to the fiery whirlpool into which it disappeared a few feet
further down; then the sparkling walls hid it from sight,
as it went on down the slope of la Sciara.

Here was the source we had been looking for!

The stolid physicist was beside himself with enthusiasm.
So it hadn't turned out a disappointment for him after
all. I was delighted for his sake as well as for mine.

The torrent flowed fast. We reckoned its speed to be
three or four miles per hour. Eleven hundred degrees, the
temperature. Width: three yards. Depth—h'm! How
were we to measure the depth? 'It came,' Pit was to say
later, with a teasing smile, to someone who was asking
him about it, 'up to our knees.'

I bent down, picked up a stone and threw it into that
glow. With my arm bent to guard my eyes, I saw the stone
bounce back off the surface like a ball on a rubber carpet!
There was something paradoxical about this elasticity of
the lava. It was amazing to see something solid bounce
back off something liquid. The fact was that this liquid
was of a density three times greater than that of the lump
of stone, which was riddled with air-holes.

Curious to see where the torrent came out again, we
made our way carefully round the tunnel, the roof of which
was only a thin basalt shell, and some paces further on
found ourselves overlooking the dizzy slopes of la Sciara.
Some thirty yards away our river of lava reappeared,
gliding steeply away downhill. Other glowing rivulets
trickled into it from left and right. All these streams, which
were quickly dimmed by a thin skin as the surface cooled
off, ran through deep channels, more or less parallel,
that furrowed the surface of the slope, sometimes running
together and joining up, and then branching out again.

About half way down, it had become a thorough-going river. In spite of the distance we could see that it was steadily slowing up. Thin, quick trickles escaped out of the congealed mass and careered off on their own, while the lava, with fresh supplies always piling up behind it, kept suddenly unleashing avalanches of incandescent blocks, which went leaping and bounding downhill in ever larger arcs, finally plunging into the sea far below.

'It must be an extraordinary sight at night,' Pit observed.

'Yes, indeed. How about having a go at it?'

'Right you are,' was his perfectly cool reply.

DESCENT TO THE VILLAGE

It was child's play going down to the village. We ran over the slope of lapilli on the eastern side of the island.[1] There was a pathway winding down. It meandered between clumps of broom, laden with masses of golden flowers, came to the vineyards, and wound its serpentine way on between the dry stone walls along the edges of the terraced fields. Twenty minutes' run from the steaming craters and the gushing lava, here everything was queerly serene: the white village, the hurried ding-dong, ding-dong of the angelus bell, and on the little square in front of the church the brown-skinned children laughing in the evening sunshine . . .

The cool, transparent sea-water washed us clean of our sweat and the sulphurous salts. And we fell asleep to the sound of the waves.

As it happened, the village was leading an abnormal life those days. A famous producer was making a film there, and with an actress who was no less famous than himself.

[1] These lapilli, varying from one to four millimetres in length, consisted of a mixture of congealed drops of lava and crystals—very fine in shape—of a mineral called augite. The augite had crystallised in the course of the years within the magma simmering away in the depths of the crater, till the day when a paroxysmal explosion had projected the whole igneous broth into the air. The violence of the blast caused by the escaping gases then pulverised the liquid lava that had congealed in the form of drops, in this way liberating the solid crystals that had already formed.

In the quiet streets that must, it seemed, be very like the streets that had been there a hundred or two hundred years earlier, one ran into generating sets and tripped over lengths of cable. In the presbytery, the only comfortable house in the place, a whole general staff had established itself, drawing up plans, considering shots, angles, sequences . . . They were arranging to have a quantity of heavy material transported to the spots that had been selected. Here preparations were being made for the work of that little army of film-technicians whose activities would in the end enable us all to behold the famous actress' despairing expressions—over life-size—on the screen.

As for the star herself, she had just gone off to Messina together with the director. Tunny-fishing was in full swing over there and they were going to 'shoot' the astonishing sight when the great net is hauled in with the enormous fish lashing about in it. But next day we met the 'chief's' right-hand man, an energetic and genial person, grey-haired, tanned, with features of classic Roman regularity.

'What we should like,' he told us, 'is to shoot the last scene, when the star is going to throw herself into the crater, at the most sensational place we can find.'

'Well, what about a place where there are torrents of lava gushing out? Right between three craters.'

'That's the very thing! Only of course you'll realise we can't risk taking our star there! It's a matter of the insurance—she's worth several million dollars. I suppose you wouldn't know some place that's still sensational, but safe?'

We thought it over. There was the interior of the great crater, but one really had to be a mountaineer to manage that. The lip of the great chimney, on the far side of il Torrione? Between two explosions—well, the danger was minimal, if not entirely non-existent, and it was relatively 'sensational'. We explained the whole thing to our very likeable new acquaintance, and worked out all sorts of schemes for him. After which we went and took a header into the blue sea.

NIGHT ON LA SCIARA

About the end of the afternoon, accompanied by one of our porters, a slim, shaggy youth with very dark eyes, we set off again, taking it easily, up the path that zigzags between the agaves and the wild fig-trees in the north-western corner of the island, slowly climbing towards the volcano. We crossed a zone where the vegetation had been ravaged by a fire the previous day. The wonderful hillside ablaze with scented broom was no longer anything but a charred slope bristling with hard stubble, the remains of the tall grasses that had been burnt. It was a startling experience to sniff again the acrid smell of bush-fires . . .

We climbed the mountain slowly. Below, almost a straight drop, the blue of the sea grew ever more and more immense. High above, great brownish coils of fumeroles were boiling up out of the craters and blowing away over the summit in the wind.

It was nine o'clock. The sun was low on the horizon. It was reflected on the endless glassy surface of the sea.

'I think this is it—isn't it?'

'Yes. We'll have to go round the side to the big shaft, and then cut across towards that rock.'

Coming down the day before we had spent a long time looking at the dizzy slopes of la Sciara, trying to make out a possible track that would enable us to get to the edge of the river of lava. Would we still be able to find our land-marks—the light rocks, white flecks of alkaline salts, sulphur deposits—when darkness fell?

The beginning was easier than we had expected. In the long twilight, following an almost horizontal line, we passed under the summit and along the upper edge of some extensive sulphur deposits, and reached the lip of the big conduit. We could hear the lava splashing in that vast hole, and that muffled sound of churning activity made us hurry on. We reached the very end of the ledge and began the climb down. Night had almost fallen. In the dark blue dusk the streams of fire were monstrous red serpents far away.

Step by step, one foot after the other, we went down the rough slope in the darkness. By now the last trace of daylight was gone, and the only glimmer we had was from the red glare of the lava on the low smoke-screen being blown this way and that in the wind.

A rocky drop in the ground, the depth of which we could not guess, worried us. With my face close to the stone, my fingers clawing at it, I explored this unknown quantity with my foot. It took us a quarter of an hour to descend ten feet. Then again there was the slope of rubble, scoriae and coarse sand. On and off these unstable screes would crumble and slide away from under our feet, dragging us away, pulling us down with them, with the same fine-drawn hissing sound that snow makes in the same circumstances. With an effort we would manage to stop ourselves, holding fast to the alpenstock or the axe. With pebbles and sand trickling and rustling all round our ankles, we would listen tensely. Supposing we suddenly started an avalanche? Then the sliding mass would gradually slow down and stop. And so we would continue on our way.

After covering some fair distance, we made a swing away over to the left, aiming for the centre of la Sciara. Now that we had the glow from the incandescent torrents, reflected on the vapour, straight ahead of us, it was more of a nuisance than a help to us and we stumbled miserably among the indescribable chaos of smashed boulders.

Suddenly, in the coolness of the night, I felt puffs of air on my face that were hot—too hot. Among the blocks I was stumbling along over there was lava, still live, burning like a sombre furnace.

'Hi, Pit! Tell Peppino to stay where he is!'

The two of us went on together. Ahead of us the jagged

ridge stood out against the diffuse crimson glimmer that
betrayed the presence of the molten river. But there was
also this furnace under our feet, with its burning breath!
A glance uphill, to the left, quickly increased our desire
to beat a retreat: glowing blocks, like *séracs* of fire, formed
the front of an outflow that was just solidifying up there.
Every moment or so one of them would break loose and
go vaulting down towards the invisible sea, lighting up
the black hillside with its leaps and bounds and scarlet
showers of sparks.

Peppino had been calmly waiting where we had left
him. Together we continued our exhausting progress over
the unstable mountain-side. We could not help feeling a
little forlorn, here in this darkness full of red glare and hot
breath, fumbling over this uncertain ground where no
human being had ever ventured before. All around us we
could feel the power of an extraordinary world on a scale
that was not our own, and absolutely indifferent to our
existence. It gave us a queer heart-ache, feeling the overwhelming grandeur of it.

'Damnation!' Tripping, I had smashed the lamp that
I was carrying fixed to my rucksack, which was to have
lighted us on our return journey. It had turned out to be
more trouble than it was worth coming down and we had
soon decided it was best to switch it off. We were going
to miss it badly in a very short time.

We had been going downhill for hours. Still we had got
no chance of moving up to the rivers of lava: what was
in our way was sometimes these sinister furnaces hidden
under an all too thin layer of blackish coke, sometimes
rocky inclines that we could not get over, sometimes
corridors of avalanches—either incandescent avalanches or
avalanches of dark and gloomy boulders. Weariness lay
heavy on my shoulders and I felt myself being slowed up
as a result of breathing this air, which was full of toxic

vapours. Thirst, too, was making itself more and more
urgently felt—that chlorine-tasting thirst one gets on active
volcanoes.

I was beginning to feel like giving up—like turning
back uphill again as soon as possible, although the very
idea of the return climb horrified me. The further down
we went, the harder and more hazardous the return would
be . . .

Pit must also be dreading the upward climb. I heard
him ask Peppino, in Italian:

'Do you think if we go right down to the sea some
fisherman might see us from his boat and come and take
us off?'

'*No. Non credo.*'

Pity . . . I too would have preferred, on the whole,
to go all the way down la Sciara del Fuoco to the sea-
shore.

Twice, three times, we had had to turn back from an
attempt to cut across the slope to the left. Suddenly,
coming out on the top of a last ridge, I found myself right
in the red blaze of the incandescent river and saw it running
along, swift and silent, only five yards ahead of me. I
went nearer still. The heat struck into my face. My eyes
were dazzled. What a vision it was!

Picciotto caught up with me. Another step . . . And
another . . . But then the burning glow of it made it
impossible to go any closer. Peppino had stopped just
behind us. Speechless, spellbound, we gazed on something
resembling the birth of our planet itself.

How many times had I already beheld such a spectacle?
But the wonder of it is new to me every time. This river
flowed along in a silence that was not silence. There was
a steady hissing that was both thin and powerful, a sound
that seemed as though in its inexorability it must be everlasting. It brought to my mind those armies of tropical
ants advancing on their irresistible march, always with
that pitiless rustling murmur . . .

I don't know how long we stayed there, staring in rapture

at this indescribable splendour, and then taking measurements, photographing, filming . . . Pit burnt the bridge of his nose by trying to get some inches nearer. Our hands holding the instruments were half toasted. The sweat poured off us. Our thirst was frightful . . . agonising . . .

After the dazzling red and yellow of the molten magma the pitch-darkness of the night into which we turned back seemed like a solid wall. We climbed uphill at random, blindly, twisting our ankles, skinning our knees, sometimes upright, more often on all fours. Scarps of rock drove us to the left; slabs of slippery smoothness sent us to the right . . . It was impossible, absolutely impossible, to find any point of reference. Sometimes we crossed ravines, sometimes we clambered up steep hillocks formed by heaps of breccia. To the right was the sheer drop into the great crater, with incandescent boulders breaking loose, like ice-blocks breaking loose from some glacier of fire and pitching headlong down the steep incline, tracing huge, bright festoons of light in the darkness.

But a rumbling sound above us made us stop short. It immediately became louder, punctuated by sharp crashes. The avalanche! We could not see anything, but the din filled our ears—even, it seemed, our bodies—so suddenly did it increase in volume. It seemed to last an age. Straining our eyes in the darkness, we were all suspense. How long it lasted! An eternity, it seemed.

Then there was a roar, and a huge, pale rock, the size of one of the houses in the village, crashed to the bottom of the corridor only five paces away from us, and then, with a colossal leap, bounced onwards downhill.

'*Pietra molto grossa*,' Peppino remarked.

We could not find the way we had come. Cliffs that we had not noticed on the way down now drove us back. We were utterly lost. Fatigue made our legs heavy, lay heavy on our shoulders.

Here was a bastion of light-coloured rock. While Pit was doing his best to get up it, I went along the base of it to the right, plunging up to the ankles in sand I could not see, glad to be able to keep one hand against the solid rock. Each of us hoped he had chosen the right way on and would not have to come back. Peppino, standing at the foot of the rock, awaited the result of our reconnoitring.

At first we kept in touch by shouting to each other. Each of us was doing his utmost, alone with his own problem. I was still making progress upwards, on all fours. Quick! I glanced swiftly upward. Yes, it looked almost as though there were a way through there . . . Oh, heavens! Here came a pack of pallid wolves swarming down on me, sulphurous vapours making a slanting attack on me in mid-climb. Should I go on? Should I get back as fast as I could? No—damn it all, I wasn't going to have climbed all this way up for nothing! So I pushed on upward, the suffocating fog catching up with me. With a handkerchief over my mouth, I climbed doggedly on. Oof! the dreadful cloud had passed.

Just at that moment, eighty or ninety feet above me, a great red cone of fire burst into the air! There was the uproar of the explosion, then the slow ascent of the incandescent clots, and finally, more and more violent, more and more concentrated, the whistling of the bombs and the crash of heavy lumps of lava falling to the ground.

No, they didn't get me that time. But I cleared out! At the bottom I found Pit, who had been driven back by insurmountable overhangs, and Peppino, composed as ever. There was nothing else to be done but to go round the bastion to the left, continuing on our endless way. For a long, long time we dragged thirstily on through that darkness, up those infernal slopes, with the ground shifting underfoot, until at last we reached the earthenware winejar that stood in a corner of our tent, full of the beautiful cold water that had been waiting there for us all the time.

MURDEROUS GASES

The sun got us out of our sleeping-bags.

Lighting the solidified alcohol under the spirit-cooker, Pit made tea with what was left of the water since the night before. Squatting on the ground, we sipped the drink gratefully. How good it seemed!

There in front of us clouds of smoke were ceaselessly unfurling over the summit and the rocky ridge that rises over it to the north, from where the track went down to San Vincenzo.

We were more or less in bliss. After the difficulties, the fears, the fiery torrents, the infernal thirst, and all the fatigues of the night, now to be here drinking this hot tea, in this magnificent early morning sunshine, gave us a feeling of intense well-being.

'Look! Mules!'

There were really mules looming up out of the smoky mist that enveloped the peak. They came at a trot, with their drivers pulling at the bridle and encouraging them with shouts. Certainly that was no place to hang about, in all those clouds of sulphur and chlorine! It was at a run that they came down the last few yards that still lay between them and our gully, and at that moment one more mule came over the top, but at a walk, and rather unsteadily. There was nobody leading it. It carried a rider. Slowly they drew nearer. Frowning in the brightness of the light, we watched this very odd rider with increasing astonishment. Then something about the man's attitude made us think there was something wrong . . . In the same moment we all got up and ran to meet him.

He literally fell into our arms. It was the film director's right-hand man, General Muratori. Livid, he just managed to gasp out: 'Fumes—air!'

There was a rattle in his throat. The muleteers gathered around us, explaining that the Commendatore had wanted to come and see for himself the place we had told him about a few days previously. But he had got caught in the blanket of gas. They had run with handkerchiefs over their mouths, but he must have taken deep breaths and got the gas right into his lungs.

It is a terrible thing to feel oneself powerless to help a human being. We tried laying him flat, sitting him up, giving him a drink of tea . . . It didn't help. The minutes passed, and he got no better. On the contrary, he seemed to be suffocating more and more. There was nothing for it, we must get him down. And as fast as possible.

Six of us carried him. We set off at top speed. Our heels dug into the black sand. We started along the path down to the village.

The sky was absolutely pure blue and as though tightly stretched. The immense sea sparkled, even more intensely blue. The world was miraculously wide and clean.

Two hundred yards further down General Muratori, having been slowly asphyxiated, died in my arms.

CHAPTER XVII

THE GREAT LORD ETNA

January 1951

ETNA HAD last year shown signs of being about to stir into life, but this time the eruption was serious. For several weeks now the lava had been trickling down the mountainside, driving the people from their vineyards and their villages. I had met my friends of Sicilian days again— Professor Abbruzzese and Professor Faraone. Picciotto, my companion on Stromboli, was to join me next day. And to help me in the work of taking notes and making films of what was going on, I had brought along with me from Paris a young man called Géry, a sun-tanned sturdy fellow who was a mountaineer and guide and who was—it should be needless to say—full of curiosity to see this sight, which for him was completely new.

Night had fallen. Fifteen yards away, the scarlet bar was advancing towards us, slowly but irresistibly. Coming down the Fontanella valley, a sort of canyon hollowed out by the spring torrents, this flow, which was for the moment the most dangerous one, was one hundred and fifty feet across and thirty high. Thirty feet is a good height: it is that of a three-storey house. I made some chalk-marks on the stones in the dry bed of the river, as points of reference. One by one the lava swallowed them up. I did a sum in my head. It was coming on at a rate of two feet a minute, which was one hundred and twenty feet an hour.

At twenty paces from this gigantic moving brazier the heat was no more than pleasant in the winter's night. At five yards, it was tropical. At four yards I just had time to make a chalk mark on the ground and glance in the view-finder of my Leica, and I was already half grilled.

This was not a wall of plastic lava progressing in the form of more or less liquid paste. The magma itself remained invisible under quantities of red-hot blocks of all shapes and sizes. But it was the magma, sliding along the bed of the Fontanella, that was driving that enormous embankment onwards, with the rivulets of burning sand oozing out here and there with a faint, insidious, almost friendly hissing. These flows of sand were the element of continuity in the progress, but it also happened from time to time that great blocks broke loose, and then there would be a muffled growl and a burst of sparks as a red, or sometimes yellow, wound opened in this monstrous dam.

Beside me were the volcanologists from the University of Catania, Doctor Abbruzzese and Professor Cumin. They had been on the spot since the beginning of the eruption—almost forty days now—observing and giving orders about protective measures and evacuation.

'I've had all I want of this!' Cumin said to me, chewing his everlasting little stumpy black cigar.

Behind us a little group of men and women stood huddled together, motionless. Some remarks uttered now and then in that rough Sicilian dialect were the only interruptions to their tragic silence. The sightseers and tourists had gone by now, and there was no one left but these rugged, dour peasants, who watched the molten rock inexorably eating up their humble fortune—vineyards, orchards, terraces that patient generations had built up on the steep sides of this narrow valley.

'Professore?'

A man draws near. Timidly, he asks if there is any hope. Is it going to stop? Is *it* going to come all the way down into the village? Fornazzo is little more than half a mile further downhill. Up to now the lava has covered almost ten

The fiery bed of Paricutin, Mexico. (*American Museum of Natural History*)
Lacroix's photograph, below, of ruins of St. Pierre after the eruption of
Mount Pelée. (*American Museum of Natural History*)

A Lacroix photograph of Mount Pelée in eruption.
(*American Museum of Natural History*)

Eruption in 1942 of Mauna Loa, Hawaii's largest volcano. (*Acme Photo*)

Night eruption of a crater within a crater of Halemaumau Volcano, Hawaii.
(*United Press Photo*)

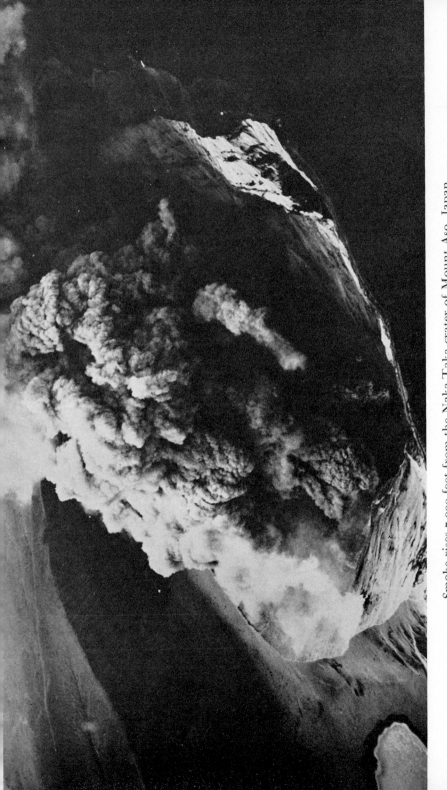

Smoke rises 7,000 feet from the Naka-Taka crater of Mount Aso, Japan.
(Signal Corps photo from Acme)

Vesuvius in 1935: ten times the normal volume of smoke accompanied a flow of molten lava. (*Keystone View Co.*)

Vesuvius in one of its greatest eruptions, photographed from an Air Force plane in 1944. (*Acme Photo*)

Another view of Vesuvius during the 1944 eruption. (*Acme Photo*)

miles since issuing from the volcanic vents. If it is to stop before reaching Fornazzo, the supply coming from the craters will have to cease. Tomorrow we shall go up and see what the future may hold in store.

'Not much hope,' Cumin replies.

Inexorably, the burning breath drives us back. The flow is steadily drawing nearer to a stone house half way up the side of the valley. Now it is almost touching it. Now it has touched it. Somewhere nearby there is a strangled sob. I turn my head and in the crimson glare I see a couple, perhaps fifty years of age, their faces twisted with anguish.

An enormous block has appeared at the top of the growing wall. It is a dark outline against the vermilion background of the smoke. This menacing tower begins to tilt over . . . Here and there its gloomy base is being sapped by the trickling away of red-hot sand. We all stand there, silent, watching, our eyes fixed on the lofty black spire.

Géry has focused his camera on it. Old hand though he is among the rocks, among sudden falls of debris and avalanches, he is so fascinated by this wild and terrible spectacle here that he has lost his usual talkativeness. He works in silence, reduced to the same humility as the *contadini* round about us.

There is a fiery flash and a narrow fissure runs from the top to the bottom of the dark tower. Only another few seconds and then, with a crash, the enormous mass splits apart, revealing a fantastic glow, and collapses in a blinding avalanche. One of the red blocks rolls and bounces to within two paces of us. The heat from it burns my face. Another, the size of a lorry, crashes into one corner of the little house. For a moment I am afraid the whole thing will come down. Then the intense yellow of the block has already faded to red, and in no time at all the black crust forms over it as it cools down and gradually goes out. The condemned cottage will not burn yet.

On the top of the lava cliff, other towers rise up. As they reach the brink, they lean over, split open with a blinding glare, and fall over with a crash, sending fringes of fire flying out around them.

We return to Zafferana, the headquarters of Catanian volcanologists. Stolidly sitting at his transmitter, a corporal is sending out in morse the bulletin that Professor Cumin has just handed him. Tomorrow morning the truckloads of carabinieri will arrive. Some more dwellings are to be evacuated . . .

Dr. Abbruzzese carries us off in his dilapidated old motor-car. The coachwork bears many an honourable scar, but the engine still does it job.

Abbruzzese, with his short Balbo-style black beard, horn-rimmed spectacles, dazzling teeth, and very faint tendency to podginess, is an alarming driver: he takes the 'blindest' hair-pin bends at full speed. The road winds round the gigantic bulk of Mount Etna. Here are apple-trees, their wintry branches bare, grey-green olive-trees, some cypresses, rising like black flames, and some umbrella pines. Then the road goes downhill awhile through dense orange-groves, a dark mass sprinkled with countless golden dots. On our right the mountainside rises sheer to the grey clouded sky.

Up to ten thousand feet, the average incline is not very considerable, but it is everywhere broken by conical hills, or rather, truncated cones—hundreds of 'parasite' volcanoes 300 to 1,200 feet high, some of which, probably thousands of years old, are under cultivation right up to their summit, while others, evidently more recent, remain black and barren against a background of vineyards and orchards.

Leaving to the left the road that leads down to Catania, we drive up a winding road. Nicolosi is the last village of any size, at an altitude of 2,750 feet. It is somewhere about here that the terrible flow burst forth which destroyed Catania in 1669. Here we take aboard our Etna guide, the sturdy Barbagallo, bronzed under his grizzled curls. The first-class metalled road winds its way between the debris of 1886 and that of 1910, those chaotic rugged piles

of black and brown blocks and scoriae; then, clearing that
zone, it leads through cultivated land again, only to plunge
once more into that sombre purgatory. Here now are the
chestnut groves, then the oak and birch woods. Giacomina
—as the motor-car is called—leaves them behind too. For
all her sixteen years, she is still full of go.

There is a sudden gust of wind. Far ahead and still
further above us, sparkling against the deep blue of the
sky, the cone appears. This is the peak of Mount Etna.

We spend the night in the refuge at la Montagnola, at
6,500 feet. As soon as day breaks we set out, in wonderful
weather, on good bearing snow, to attack the three thousand
and more feet between us and the observatory built right
at the foot of the last cone. The team is now differently
made up, Cumin and Abbruzzese having been replaced
by Faraone and Picciotto. We walk fast, anxious to get
within sight of the events that are in eruption. But how can
one help stopping to admire this snowy splendour? An
immense panorama spreads out ten thousand feet below—
the Bay of Catania, the Bay of Syracuse, the twinkling of
the Simeto River and, away towards Enna, the long brown
and dark green range of hills.

On our right twin columns rise above the white
peak to which we are steadily drawing nearer: one is of
white vapour, a dazzling cumulus with blue-grey shadows
in its folds, and the other is brown and thick, being driven
up in furious puffs that swirl out in dark eddies. The first
must emanate from the secondary vents that are emitting
the lava flows. The second, which is heavy with dust, is
probably rising from the explosive chimney.

We are making for the Mount Etna volcanological
observatory, an impressive concrete cube surmounted by

a hemispherical dome. It is built on a vast ledge at the foot of the cone at the mountain's peak. As we pass, we admire the steel shutters that protect the double windows, the double doors, and the thickness of the walls (which measure more than three feet through). But why is this fortress empty? Faraone gives us the answer to the riddle: no money! The plan had been to instal laboratories (he explains to us), put in running water, and fit the place up with central heating. But alas, all this had to be abandoned in 1940, and after the war there were no funds, so that this superb building remains bare, with no trace of a scientific instrument in it.

In the kitchen we find a little stock of porridge-oats that I left there last year, in December 1949, when I came to observe the little eruption. Since the porridge has been waiting for us, let's eat it. The Italians are not used to this sort of food. They make a polite show of enjoying the thick gruel. We talk for a while, but then the important thing is—rest. Tomorrow is going to be a hard day.

We get up at two in the morning. The moon, which is in its last quarter, is not the only light we have on setting forth: there is a wild red glow in the eastern sky. In the icy darkness the thickness of our figures, muffled as we are in scarves, padded jackets and helmets, makes me think of some antarctic expedition. It seems a little odd, encountering a temperature of minus 15 degrees centigrade in Sicily.

Ten thousand feet below, twelve miles away, the lights of Catania are twinkling, and the villages and hamlets are like other, smaller nebulae in a universe of darkness.[1]

A very strong wind is blowing at our backs, a blizzard, indeed, driving the snow from the high slopes. What an austere peak this is . . . Then we enter the upper part of

[1] Walking eastwards, we soon went over a ridge and saw a new and considerable 'nebula', this time 'in profile'. It was Reggio di Calabria, nearly forty-five miles away on the other side of the Straits of Messina.

a vast depression, the valley del Leone. At our feet, some hundreds of yards distant, we suddenly catch sight of the explosive vent.

It is a red mouth with a terrific column of black smoke issuing from it. Every two or three seconds the crater vomits out a crimson bubble that quickly swells up and bursts in a violent puff of gas. A burst of incandescent blocks shoots up to a height of seventy or eighty feet, then falls in dense showers. Our nostrils are filled with the smell of sulphuretted hydrogen.

There is still more than a quarter of a mile between us and the vent itself. We hurry down the slope, over the hard snowy surface that is strewn with ashes. Sometimes our heels burst through the surface shell, leaving light footmarks where we have passed. We are now less than a hundred yards from the crater.

In the darkness the fine lapilli, those pin-heads of congealed silica, rained down unendingly from the black plume of smoke that suddenly hid the moon from our sight. The smell of sulphuretted hydrogen had gone, and was replaced by the acrid odour of sulphur dioxide. I noticed that the blackened snow was riddled with holes, where bombs had fallen. Stopping, I got my steel helmet out of my rucksack and put it on.

The ground was now level. I advanced with care. Lapilli were falling in dense showers, drumming on our helmets.

More slowly still, I approached the mouth of the volcano. I felt a great desire to glance inside and see the level at which the lava was boiling. The information would be useful in forecasting the duration of the eruption. But the smoke and dust formed an opaque screen, which was torn only by explosions.

There was a whistling sound and then a thud close to me. It was the first bomb. I was no longer used to this sort of thing, and my heart began to beat fast . . .

After a moment's pause, I moved on, feeling the ground quivering under my feet. A fraction of a second later the explosion burst forth out of the crater.

I was now warned of every burst by one of these little muffled tremors. A hail of projectiles came down not far away, and some fell right behind me. It would be rash to go further forward. I spent two or three minutes—on the alert for falling projectiles all the time—taking some shots with my movie-camera. Close behind me, devilishly close, indeed, for a newcomer, Géry was shooting a film. Beside him, Picciotto was taking photographs and making notes. Faraone and the three porters remained a hundred paces away.

A shower of live embers came down all round me. One of them bounced and hit me on the thigh.

I decided to do without a glance into the crater, and beat a retreat.

We moved all round the explosive vent. Every so often we had to turn back and try in other places because of the crevasses in the basalt, which were treacherously concealed under the blanket of snow. Volcanic vapours blew about everywhere in the wind, sinister in the darkness.

We were moving along a surface of black snow, at an incline of between 40 and 45 degrees. Thanks to our ice-axe, Géry and I could slide along and pull ahead of our companions, who were prudently roped together. There below us, yellow with heat, was the vent from which the lava flowed. The topography of the eruption was clear. There was a radial fracture in the gigantic cone of Etna; in the upper part of it, at an altitude of 8,800 feet, there was the explosive crater, out of which the gases escaped more or less violently, drawing out with them some of the magma, which was shattered to fragments by the force of the explosions; in the lower part, at 7,200 feet, the lava flowed out as though from some lofty Cyclopean furnace.

I wanted to look inside that cauldron. I could already hear the tremendous panting of it. Step by step I crept down the snow, which was hard as ice. Still five yards to go. Now four . . . I could still see nothing but the thick column of vapour belched out of the pit with a kind of strange hastiness. Yet another step. Heavens, how hard the snow was! I craned forward, trying to see over the black rim of the cauldron, to see what magical brew it contained. I remembered the fascination with which Richard and I had stood motionless a few yards from Kituro's crater, filled with boiling gold.

It was no good. Here the vapour was so dense that the most I could get was, now and then, a shadowy glimpse of the mighty frothing there below.

A step hacked out in the snow with the axe made it possible to take one more step forward. It was important not to slip. Two fathoms straight below my feet was the gasping maw, yawning open. Anchored a few feet higher up, with his eye to the view-finder of his camera, Géry called out to me:

'If you're going to fall, let me know. I wouldn't want to miss a shot like that!'

I was not particularly keen on imitating the beautiful film star. Observing great care, I returned uphill.

The night is nearly over. We hurry to get round the little cone, in the top of which the crater is overflowing. We make a detour to the left, then go eastwards in the direction of the outflows. The snow has given way to unsteady slopes of scoriaceous blocks, where we trip and stumble. A gust of sulphurous gas, blown down the wind, chokes us for a moment, and then suddenly, after crossing a last rocky ridge, we are confronted with the fantastic vision of two terrifying streams of liquid fire.

One of them, bright scarlet, flows straight towards us, but then, only several paces away, joins up with the other, which is also quite near by. This second stream is so hot that it is yellowish gold in colour, and so liquid that it runs down the mountainside, from our right to our left, at the speed of water flowing over the top of a weir. I have never before seen a river of lava flow at such a rate. We calculate that this red-hot flood is travelling nearly twenty miles an hour, and perhaps more. It is hard to say exactly.

I take another step forward, and the wall of heat pulls me up short. Beyond this point—experience has taught me—the radiant heat burns without mercy. I focus the electric pyrometer on the molten matter, and even before I can take a reading, my hands are roasted, in spite of the protective gloves. Before I can get the measurements, I have to fall back a pace. On the red I read 980 degrees, then 940 degrees, then 1,010 degrees, on the yellow 1,120 degrees, 1,090 degrees, 1,110 degrees centigrade.

At this moment the wind changes, blowing the fumes down on us. Bent double, racked by agonising coughs, we feel as if each spasm were scraping our lungs out with emery-paper. In vain we try to breathe some clean air in through our handkerchiefs. We have to run away in order to recover. After a while, however, we go back to the streams. Again the gas makes an onslaught on us, we gasp, we struggle, we run away, and again we return to the attack. It is dawn, and yet the light of the sun has not dimmed that of the incandescent lava.

The river of fire spreads out in the enormous Val del Bove. Far away, hundreds and hundreds of yards below where we stand, the red-hot glow of the magma disappears gradually under a crust as it cools down, reappearing here and there in the mist of the vast dispersion of sombre basalt.

This grandiose sight will unfortunately not help us to reassure the terrified people down below, on our return. The fluidity of the lava, the intensity of its rate of discharge, which we reckon to be about a million cubic yards per hour, the high temperature at the emission vent, the frequency of the micro-seismic shocks, its high gaseous content—none of these things makes it seem at all likely that the eruption will slow up in the near future.

When we were standing before the Fontanella outflow, we still had some hope that the lava might stop before it destroyed the beautiful orchards, the well-tended vineyards, and the chestnut groves further down the mountainside. Here we know that it is all under sentence of death. We know that away down there the roads will be swallowed up and yet more houses buried.

It is eleven o'clock when we finally leave the surroundings of these fantastic springs, exhausted as we are from the gases and the heat. Keeping as close as possible to the edge of the river, we go downhill, passing two magnificent series of rapids, rather like cataracts of fire, where the red-hot lava regains its terrifying original speed. And I notice that my thick canvas windbreaker is so charred that it is falling to pieces, thinner and more delicate than gauze. In a moment my companions begin quarrelling over the remnants of that once handsome garment—a souvenir! a souvenir! So I continue on my journey almost in rags.

In the distance the sea twinkles in the sunlight. But we are still under the shadow of the plume of smoke and ashes. The strange mist of fine lapilli drifts ceaselessly around us. A thousand yards above us now, the crater is still spitting out its column of brown ink, and from here we can see the enormous truncated cone as a whole—a new mountain added to the gigantic bulk of Etna.

It is not till thirteen hours after our nocturnal departure that we reach the main road. At that same moment the red tongue of the flow slides under the bridge across the ravine. Never again will the spring floods ripple under it.

Further down, and on the edges of the lava flow, men are hastily slashing down apple-trees, oaks and chestnuts. Others are trying to dig up some few of their precious vines from the fertile humus that this catastrophic river is going to cover up for ever. Children tear at the grass, trying to save some scraps of hay. Nearby groups of silent people stand motionless, watching the monster engulf man's handiwork.

CHAPTER XVIII

THE SPIRIT OF EMPEDOCLES

WE CANNOT take any counter-action against an earthquake, a tidal wave, or a volcanic eruption. The millions of horse-power or kilowatts that science has domesticated are mere trifles compared with the omnipotence that is displayed in the faintest jerk or shudder of the globe itself. Still, it is not in the nature of man to fold his hands in his lap when he is faced with something that at first seems beyond his power to cope with. He has tamed the sea, conquered the Poles, and he is now completing his victory over the mountains.

But the volcanic peril does not wait for man. It does not menace only those reckless persons who insist on playing with fire . . . Human history is full of stories echoing with the cry of buried towns. To the sinister memories of Laki, Krakatoa, and St. Pierre we may add another, that of Etna in 1669, which engulfed part of Catania, destroyed more than fifty towns and three hundred villages, and caused a hundred thousand deaths. Such catastrophes are explained by the snare that lies for swarming humanity in the exceptional fertility of volcanic regions. The dragon's teeth, whether or not it was Jason who sowed them, in the Caucasus or elsewhere, have always produced a rich crop of men.[1] For if lava is barren of ore, by its very nature,

[1]The Caucasus is a volcanic region that is at present dormant, but which was active in Antiquity. Jason on his quest for the Golden Fleece, Jason

which excludes the possibility of concentrations of metal, it compensates by producing particularly rich arable land, which is constantly regenerated and enriched by the dust ejected at each new eruption, which includes lime, potassium, and phosphates. Azote is about the only thing lacking to make these showers of ashes a complete natural manure. Their physical texture makes for a light soil, easily penetrated by air and water. The fine quality of the mineral particles of which they consist causes them to be acted on very rapidly by the atmosphere, and plants are soon able to draw from them the salts that are indispensable to growth. Vines, corn, rice and coffee flourish wonderfully on such soil. Farming peoples have always worked these inexhaustible lands, in Java as in Sicily, and if they do not make a better living from them, it is certainly for reasons that have nothing to do with the richness of the soil. But do not these reasons exist elsewhere as well? And why should they leave regions where Nature, at least, is generous to them? Generous . . . Until the moment, that is, when the scourge that was the origin of their prosperity once more makes itself felt. It would be a wonder if man did not dream of some day acquiring knowledge that will enable him to foresee these reawakenings and, if the fields cannot be protected, at least save thousands of lives.

Fertile though they are—the reader will object—these murderous regions could perfectly well be abandoned and their population transferred far out of the range of the fire. But supposing a volcano rises up where nobody was expecting anything of the kind? Etna and Vesuvius are known; they are old enemies. But nobody expected Jorullo. It appeared in Mexico on the 28th September 1759, and forty years afterwards it was still in eruption (a short time later Humboldt was to visit this terrible child sprung fully armed from the womb of the earth). It sometimes happens

sowing dragon's teeth from which armed men sprang—have we not here the showers of volcanic ashes that burn but also produce fertile soil that rapidly becomes populated?

that islands rise up out of the water where no island was before. There is Bogoslof in the Aleutian archipelago, a little island between Malta and Sicily, another that emerged only as recently as 1950 in the Sea of Azov, off the coast of the Crimea. These are true geographic creations, the only phenomena that nowadays enable man to imagine what the great geological upheavals may have been like to look at.[1] Stupefied, modern man sees *new mountains* appearing on the surface of the earth, which he had believed was finally established in its present form. He gives them names expressive of his amazement: Monte Nuovo rose to the West of Naples in the sixteenth century; Novarupta, in mid-twentieth century, came bristling up out of the Valley of Ten Thousand Vapours in Alaska. And then there is Parícutin.

Once upon a time, near a village in the south-western part of Mexico, a peasant, Dionisio Polido, was digging his field. For some days he had noticed thin cracks here and there among the furrows. Sometimes little wisps of faintly warm smoke escaped through them. Like a good worker, Dionisio did not ask questions, but went on with his job. With a rough spade, he shovelled earth over the cracks and stamped them down. Then, satisfied with his handiwork, he came with his wife and son to contemplate the well-tilled field. At that moment a terrifying growl issued from the depths of the earth. Dionisio, his wife and their son, fled as fast as their legs would carry them. It was the 20th February 1943. Parícutin was being born. It rose to a height of more than twelve hundred feet, covered several thousand acres with its lava, including the village, and still has not finished spitting forth fire.

Whether it is on spots still virgin of volcanic activity, or in the neighbourhood of long-feared craters, are we condemned always to be taken by surprise, crushed, shrivelled by burning cinders, or engulfed in a flood of fire? Will the nightmare of Herculaneum and Pompeii always wake the women and children too late?

[1] However profoundly different their genesis may have been.

Even then, in that night of terror, one man's gaze remained calm and clear. Instead of fleeing in the galley he was aboard, Pliny studied the flame-gashed cloud; while all the others made their escape, he disembarked at Stabia and walked to meet the cataclysm, noting the smallest details and dictating his observations as he went. And this was, of course, because he had set himself the task of recording everything that seemed curious and worthy of remark. What a pity we do not possess the tablets of Pliny the Elder! But at least the famous letter written by his nephew to Tacitus contains precious information, together with the account of his death: here are the first beginnings of a science to which mankind is indebted for its escape from the rage of more than one Vesuvius.

In this struggle between the population of the earth and its terrible adversary, science gives us two of the good boxer's main aids in warding off the swiftest and most damaging blows: foresight and speed. It gives us fore-knowledge of volcanic awakenings, thanks to methods of investigation that we owe to physics and chemistry. It gives us speed in our modern methods of evacuating the danger-zones.

There is an increasingly large number of instruments that enable us to forecast eruptions: seismographs, micro-phones, magnetic balances, gravimeters, spectroscopes, and so on. A volcano that is carefully watched cannot take us by surprise, and we are even able to forecast the degree of violence the eruption will have. Once the cataclysm has been foreseen, nothing should prevent us from using 'air-lifts', originally devised and perfected for quite different purposes, in order to save human lives.

It may seem a little utopian today to suggest it would be better to build volcanological observatories rather than block-houses, and to recommend a peaceful use for aircraft carriers . . . Nevertheless, there is not much doubt what answer one would get from the tens of millions of those who live in volcanic countries. I am well aware that the danger of which I am speaking is not very likely to affect the imagination of those who have become slowly immunised to horror by the headlines of sensational newspapers. But that is doubtless only a transitory paralysis of the emotions, and one need not, perhaps, yet despair of the future of the human species—a future closely bound up with the awakening of man's vigilance on all planes.

More than one government has tried, before now, to work out schemes for the safeguarding of the populations over which the volcanoes loom with the perpetual threat of eviction and worse. Apart from the purely scientific observatories like those on Vesuvius, in Hawaii and on Kamchatka, well-equipped stations and various minor depots have been set up in the East Indies and in Japan. The Dutch government organised a whole system of warnings and evacuation in order to avoid the catastrophes that had all too often ravaged the European plantations and the Malayan villages. Since 1916 the first observatory has been keeping watch on the volcano Idjen.

Idjen's crater contains a lake, the water of which contains 10 per cent sulphuric acid. Before the safeguard system was put into operation, this lake overflowed in the heavy rains, poisoning the local rivers. A sluice was therefore built, and a rather strange one, the bricks being made of a mixture of sand and sulphur solution. This very special sort of concrete resists the corrosive action of the acid in the lake water. At a suitable time the sluice is opened, letting the water through into a canal that conducts the overflow straight into the sea. There is however another threat occasioned by the very existence of this lake, as by all lakes that form in craters: when an eruption takes place the water is violently ejected, devastating the surrounding areas with *lahars*, torrents of mud sweeping along enormous blocks of rock, which are almost as much to be feared as the 'burning clouds'. My friend Richard told me that the lake in the Kloet volcano in this way caused a whole series of disasters in the course of the past century. In 1919 several tunnels were constructed, by means of which it was gradually possible to reduce the water level; and it is hoped that this will diminish the destructive effect of future *lahars*.

The famous volcano Semeru now has on its sides a string of observation-posts that are connected by telephone with the neighbouring valleys. Here the danger was the muddy avalanches caused by heavy rains falling on the enormous quantities of debris that accumulated from successive eruptions. In order to protect the population, it was decided to build hills high enough for them to take refuge on when given sufficient warning. In the course of the years observation-posts of this kind have been set up around the principal volcanic craters in the Indonesian archipelago, besides which first-rate scientific observatories now exist on the chief volcanoes in the East Indies, Papandayan, Tangkoeban Praheo, Kawah Kamodyang, Lamongan, and Merapi.

This last crater is almost continuously in the throes of terrible eruptions. Day and night the observatory staff are busy recording everything that may herald a paroxysm: the nature and intensity of the sounds produced by the explosions, the direction and violence of the discharges from the explosions, variations in meteorological data, the temperature of such of the volcanic vapours as are accessible, and seismograms registering the earth-tremors. Advance posts are linked by telephone to headquarters, and daring volcanologists patrol the sides of the cone, venturing even into the interior of the crater in order to get as many indications and measurements as is humanly possible. An absolutely hermetic underground shelter, equipped with oxygen cylinders, enables the observers to remain there as long as possible, even in the case of an eruption. There is a seismologist there, who is in touch with the valley by telephone. Thanks to all this work, eruptions can be forecast and the population evacuated in time, so that there is no longer any danger beyond that of damage done to property.

Obviously, the job these observers have is not entirely devoid of danger. The man who goes and takes the temperature of volcanic vapours, craters and molten lava must have pretty good nerves . . . Nevertheless, the danger is not really greater than that run by miners exposed to firedamp, quarrymen handling dynamite, fishermen on the high seas, or pedestrians hurrying across the Place de la Concorde at midday. The death of one individual like General Muratori, or of one American professor and his sixteen students, who were unexpectedly overtaken by a red-hot torrent on the slopes of the Colombian volcano Purace on the 26th May 1949, is to be attributed to their not knowing what precautions to take. To my knowledge only one experienced volcanologist has died the victim of a volcano, and that was a Danish professor who was struck on the head by a bomb while he was filming the eruption of Mount Hekla in 1947. The mortality among several hundreds of professionals engaged in this work seems inconsiderable. One must bear in mind that every volcanologist who returns to civilisation may get himself run over by a motor-car . . . Think of that great navigator, Dumont d'Urville, who discovered so many unknown shores and braved the ice-packs of the Antarctic, and who died in a railway accident in the suburbs of Paris.

All the same, there is no doubt that a spice of danger does to a certain extent—anyway, at the beginning—play its part in deciding one to begin studying volcanoes. For there is something terrifying about even very minor manifestations of this blind and inordinate power. Of course, the aspiring geologist knows from geophysics that the crust of the earth is no more than a very thin shell, which is always in danger of being broken by the vitrous fluid that rises to terrific temperatures and even more terrific pressure. Nevertheless, in so far as this is something the volcanologist has learnt merely from books, the fact does not impinge on his emotions: the shell is an image, and a sane man is not frightened of images. We are by instinct too sure of the solidity of 'the ground beneath our feet'. But the earth only has to start shaking enough to sway the sheltering walls around us, and from some unplumbed depths of our being a vague horror arises, a horror so intense that all other fears are nothing in comparison. This dread, with a kind of secret exaltation that goes with it, is always waiting somewhere at the back of the mind of any man who takes on the task of coming to grips with a volcano, living within sound of its rumblings, going through its fumes and gases, drawing near to those fiery rivers that may always overtake one. Such a man goes about his job unarmed and vulnerable, as it were, in the immediate proximity of a cunning monster whose reactions have nothing in common with our scale of things and our strength. In all ages volcanoes have frightened, fascinated and attracted man, because what they hold is at once terrifying, splendid and mysterious.[1]

A great sense of wonder, a slight taste for danger, and the attraction of the unknown—this, I think, is the combination that gives rise to a passion for volcanoes. Then, in the course of becoming familiar with them and making them the subject of thorough study, the volcanologist becomes so preoccupied with questions of *why* and *how* that there is no room left in his mind for anything else. He has now entered the second phase, which is that of scientific knowledge, one that demands methodical work, discipline, conscientiousness, and the humility that is necessary for going on and on with precise measurements. This is perhaps the most absorbing phase, though it is also often the most disappointing, when one tries to arrive at some general understanding of what happens, tries to classify, define, suggest causes, note variations and in-variables, and also to forecast.

One of the most eminent volcanologists this century has known was the American Frank Perret, a Frenchman by birth. He was an electrical engineer who abandoned his laboratory and exchanged his career for another on hearing the news of the eruption of Mount Pelée. Four years later, in 1906, he became famous throughout the scientific world

[1] Of two celebrated novels in which volcanoes play a principal part, one, Bulwer-Lytton's *The Last Days of Pompeii*, deals with the terrifying aspect, and the other, Jules Verne's *Journey to the Centre of the Earth*, is inspired by the fascination that volcanic mysteries exercise over our questing minds.

for his observations, made at close quarters, of a serious eruption of Vesuvius. It was well-deserved fame, and it continued to grow. Until his death recently, Perret travelled about visiting volcanic regions all over the world. His wide knowledge of eruptive manifestations more than once enabled him to warn the local inhabitants of an approaching cataclysm. On other occasions, as for instance at Martinique in 1929, after spending several days studying the eddies of smoke and dust issuing from the volcano, and the rumblings it emitted, he was in a position to reassure the inhabitants and get them to return to the town they had abandoned; for his observations had convinced him that the showers due to fall from the burning cloud brooding overhead would come down on a desert region. Some days later his predictions were fulfilled to the letter.

Through the work of men like Perret, volcanology has become a science, one that is steadily striving towards greater exactitude and thoroughness in the forecasting of eruptions. Formerly, like all branches of 'natural history', volcanology was mainly descriptive. So it was, for instance, for that Lord Hamilton, ambassador to the Kingdom of Naples, who made a minutely detailed painting of Vesuvius, Etna and Stromboli, that trinity of fire in the Mediterranean. At that epoch volcanoes still belonged to the realm of geography. The great Alexander Humboldt took an intense interest in the subject during a journey he made to South America and Mexico between 1799 and 1803. With his friend Aimé Bonpland, the French botanist, he climbed to the peak of Teneriffe, visited the 'volcanitos' region of Columbia, and in the Andes observed Cotopaxi, Antisana, Chimborazo, and that grim Purace that was to engulf seventeen all too daring explorers, a hundred and fifty years later. The account he gives of his ascent to the crater of Pichincha, which no one but La Condamine had ever had a sight of before, is in its sober way a very revealing example of the impassioned curiosity and wary venturesomeness that drive the naturalist towards volcanoes: 'Three peaks, three rocks, arise out of the ring of the crater itself, towering up over the abyss; there is no snow on them because the vapours exhaled from the mouth of the volcano always melt it. I climbed one of these rocks, and found on its summit a rock that, being supported only on one side and undermined below, hung out over the precipice in the manner of a balcony. However, this stone is only about twelve feet long and six broad, and is constantly being severely shaken by earth-tremors, of which we counted eighteen in less than thirty minutes. In order to get a better view of the bottom of the crater, we lay flat on our bellies and peered over the edge. I do not think the imagination can paint a picture of anything more desolate, mournful and terrifying than what we there beheld. The mouth of the volcano is a circular orifice about three miles in circumference, surrounded by sheer cliffs the top of which is covered with snow. The interior is pitch dark. But the pit itself is so immense that one can distinguish the peaks of several mountains standing within it, their summits seeming to be three hundred fathoms below us. From this one can imagine where their base must be!'

Is not the modern scientist's eager gaze, his peering into the unfathomable pit, in the living tradition of that bygone Empedocles of twenty centuries ago? Empedocles, so the story goes, spent years on the smoking summit of gigantic Etna, till the day when the over-daring observer was swallowed up in the crater. And the legend adds that all the volcano left of him was his sandals. I cannot say that I have seen the sandals of Empedocles, but a year before the last eruption, the most considerable in this half-century, which took place in December 1949, I had been called to the scene by the news that an outburst was imminent, and explored all that high region of colossal rubble, where immense saurians of black lava slept in the snowy expanses, and there I was shown the *Torre de Filosofo*, the Philosopher's Tower. At an altitude of over 9,500 feet, it is one of hundreds of outcrop cones that form bosses on that enormous cap. Was it here that the sage of old built himself a shelter, having withdrawn far from the bustle of towns? For a week we prowled about this amazing world on the heights of Mount Etna, from where one can see over whole provinces and has a glimpse of three seas. . . . What thoughts must Empedocles have had, all alone up there, bronzed by the sunshine, battered by icy hurricanes, face to face with that mysterious fire?

Where others saw nothing but some Cyclops' blazing eye, heard only the hammering in Vulcan's smithies far below, the ancient philosopher must have guessed at some physical secret to which only observation could give him the key. Grand old Empedocles, hero and first martyr in the cause of a science of volcanoes! It is only proper that his legendary figure should be recalled to memory here on this last page, and that honour should be done to a mind that was not content with hearsay, but insisted on *knowing for itself*.

EXPLANATORY NOTES

(*a*) Lapilli are small drops of lava, the size of a pea or even smaller, that are flung off from the liquid column of lava in the course of eruption; they begin their flight through the air in a liquid state and cool off and harden before they fall. These droplets are formed whenever the emission of gases is sufficiently violent to at least partially pulverise the liquid lava in the crater. There are also lapilli that are ejected already in a solid state: these are minerals that have crystallised while still in the fluid magma. A very vigorous eruption reduces the liquid to droplets, so liberating the crystals. On Stromboli there are thick layers of such lapilli, some of them little glassy bubbles, full of air-cavities and very light, and some of them augite crystals, measuring from 2 to 5 millimetres in length.

(*b*) The globe is encased in a crystalline crust, varying from 25 to 50 miles in thickness. As the diameter of the earth is 4,100 miles, it is no exaggeration to compare its crust to the shell of an egg. Under this thin crystalline crust, which is solid in the physical sense of the word, there are layers—some hundreds of miles thick—of non-crystalline vitrous rocky substance, known as the coat. These layers of magma go down to a depth of 1,800 miles. And the centre of the planet is a nucleus whose physical properties are still almost unknown to us.

Whereas the crust is mainly composed of rocks of an average density of about 2·7, whose normal chemical composition is *acidic*, as is for instance that of the granites or the rhyolite lavas, the *coat* of vitrous magma directly underneath this has a density of about 3 and a very *basic* composition similar to that of the basalts. The name SIAL has been given to the rocks of the acidic crust, in reference to the fact that their essential elements are silica (Si) and aluminium (Al), and SIMA to the basic vitreous coat extending from the crust to the periphery of the nucleus, because it consists chiefly of silica and magnesium. Sima is vitreous. It is subjected to terrific hydrostatic pressure in the region of tens of thousands of pounds per square inch; its temperature exceeds 2,000 degrees centigrade. All this gives it properties that seem fairly strange if we compare them to the scale of things in our world, which is under the pressure of the atmosphere. Sima is hundreds of times more rigid than steel at a normal temperature, and at the same time it can flow like a liquid; indeed, it is actually a liquid, since it is vitreous and not crystalline.

Deep basic magma behaves like a fluid when force is applied to it for a long time, even though the intensity of the pressure from below may be slight; it behaves like an extremely rigid solid when it is short. It breaks (causing a seismic shock) when the pressure is violent and short, but it will flow under a slight pressure constantly brought to bear throughout thousands of years.

In contact with the crust, and especially under the great oceans, the upper level of the magma has the tendency to cool off, its heat being radiated through the earth's crust and out into interplanetary space. On the other hand, at the lower level, where the coat is in contact with the very great heat of the nucleus, the sima is always heating up. Its *cold* part, which is the more dense and therefore also the heavier, is situated above the hotter and therefore lighter part. Here, then, is a disequilibrium contrary to the laws of gravitation. But as the sima is a fluid, currents come into existence within it, tending to restore the equilibrium. Columns of light, hot matter begin to rise, and similar columns of cooler, heavier matter begin to sink. *Convection currents* come into existence, forming bubbles similar to those that arise in a kettle of water gently heated on a fire. Calculations made by geophysicists give us cause to think that there are currents moving at a speed of several inches a year, and these currents bring terrific force, amounting to between 30,000 and 150,000 tons per cubic inch, to bear on the base of the crystalline crust, under which horizontal ramifications interconnect the light ascending columns and the concentric layers of cooler substance descending.

These upheavals are sufficient to cause displacements in areas where the crust of the earth is weak and relatively plastic, as the *orogenic* zones are: these deep marine depressions are due to the upward pressure on the floor of the sea that is brought about by the convergence of two descending currents. Although sediment brought down by the rivers of the neighbouring continents accumulates to a thickness of thousands of feet on the floor

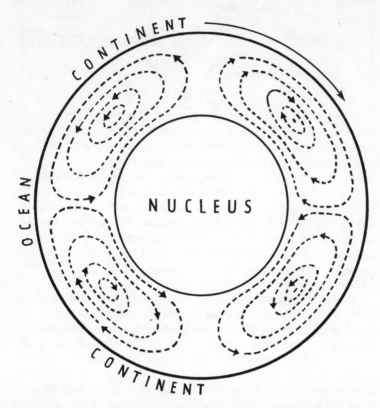

of the sea, over these currents, *the depth of the marine depression never becomes less in all these millions of years*, for underneath this accumulation of sediment the crust curves away downward under the influence of the downward pull of the convection currents of the sima. These depressions, which are called *geosynclinal*, are mountain ranges in process of being born. In fact, when the thermal equilibrium is finally restored in the vitreous magma, after millions of years, the currents will stop and the forces of Archimedes' law (known in geophysics as isostasis), which up to then have been

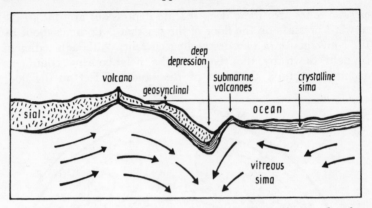

frustrated, will again come into operation; the sediment that has piled up, crushed under intense pressure, will rise again, emerge from the water and tower up as mountain ranges.

Nevertheless, in the first stage, when the convection currents are in operation, terrific *tensions* are at work in the earth's crust up above them, that is to say, in relation to the directions of the currents, *behind* the zones under pressure. When these tensions exceed the limits of the crystalline crust's elasticity, they cause networks of great fractures to come about within the crust; and through these fractures the sima rises to the surface, thus producing *orogenic* volcanic activity.

Extremely high tensions may also operate, not only in zones where the earth's crust is weak and easily changed in shape, but under rigid areas, under the old bases or footings of oceans and continents. Under the oceans, where the cooling down of the sima immediately below the crust is at its maximum, hot currents coming up from great depths will spread out in all directions. The enormous tensions caused by this divergence will tend to break the solid crust after constricting it, perhaps in the same way that the application of divergent forces breaks a test-tube by creating resistance. These fractures occur more readily under the oceans, where the crystalline crust is thinner than that forming the continents. In fact we can observe that the floors of the great oceans are gashed by huge rectilinear fractures, out of which volcanic islands arise. There are, besides, very many submarine volcanoes that never reach the surface of the water, which are just beginning to be discovered by ultrasonic soundings; they also rise out of fissures in the ocean bed.

To sum up: convection currents exist within the sima, a tremendously viscous thick layer between the central nucleus of the earth and the thin envelope (sial) that forms its outer skin. These currents cause great pressure on certain areas of the earth's crust, bringing about marine depressions as a result of the upward movement resulting from the convergence of descending currents. These depressions then cause hypertension in other zones, with resulting volcanic activity.

(*c*) The total volume of lava emitted by the two vents, Kituro and Muhuboli, was in the region of 30 million cubic yards, or 78 million tons. It is very much more difficult to estimate the volume of gas, especially in conditions as unfavourable as mine, for I was without instruments or co-workers. Basing my calculation partly on the approximate speed of the jets of gas, whether continuous or explosive, and partly on the surface area of the vents through which these gases escaped, I arrived at a volume of about 20 thousand million cubic yards. If we take the density of these gases to be 0·18, their weight will be 24 million tons.

This gives the proportion of gas to lava as 31 to 100.

In the great eruption of Nyamlagira in 1938–39 this proportion, according to the volcanologist Verhoorgen, did not exceed 1 to 100. The Kituro eruption therefore gives an exceptionally high proportion of gas to lava, if it is borne in mind that it was a volcano of the effusive type, like the majority of those rising from the fractures that gash the bases of continents and oceans, and not explosive, as are the volcanoes along the *fringes* of the great Pacific, Atlantic, and Indian Oceans.

(*d*) In all probability a sink-hole of this kind comes about as the result of a subsidence of the area around the crater, after the withdrawal of the column of magma that feeds the volcano. This withdrawal leaves a void, and the accumulated layers of consolidated flows and ashes forming the dome of the volcano, no longer being supported in the centre, collapse into this void. Thus a sub-circular depression comes into existence, often a mile or more wide, seemingly cut vertically by some giant with a die-stamp.

These sink-holes are characteristic of volcanoes of the Hawaiian type (Kilaua, Mauna Loa, Savai, etc.), to which both our active volcanoes in the Virunga Range, Nyamlagira and Niragongo, belong.

There are other types of so-called craters, the caldeiras or calderas, to give them their proper name; they are cauldrons where violent explosions take place. To these belong Teneriffe, Krakatoa, Santorin in the Cyclades, the enormous Ngorongoro and Menengai in Eastern Africa, Katmai in Alaska, and many others.

In current usage, however, the term caldera is applied to what should really be called a sink-hole, if the cavity (as in the case of Nyamlagira) results from a collapse and not from an evisceration.

(*e*) In this connection it is perhaps interesting to note that three levels of increasing altitude—Muhuboli about 5,250 feet, Kituro about 5,900, and the fissures that came into existence in May, rising from 5,900 to 6,500 feet—are associated with the emission of increasingly large quantities of gas and correspondingly less and less lava. The Muhuboli eruption was almost exclusively of lava, with extremely little gas; that of Kituro gave 30 per cent weight of gas in relation to the flows and ejecta; the parasitic vents higher up produced only gas, without any liquid or solid matter whatsoever. In view of this, one would like to consider the possibility of a reservoir chamber of magma, a thousand or even several thousand feet under the surface of the earth, in which the magma separates into various substances—certain heavy minerals, like augite and olivine, being the first to crystallise into the vitreous mass, whereas the volatile elements, chloride, sulphur dioxide and carbon dioxide, azote, and hydrochloric acid, emerge from solution and collect under the roof of the reservoir until the moment when an opening—caused by the pressure they exert or by the thrust of the column of magma— allows them to escape into the atmosphere.

(*f*) These *dikes* are nothing more or less than seams of igneous rock. They are originally caused by lava that at some time filled up the fissures gashing the walls of the crater—at a time, that is, when the crater was completely full of magma—which in all probability were the passages through which exterior emissions came. After having entered into these faults, the lava cooled down very slowly, on account of the isolating property of the rocks surrounding it, and the slowness of the cooling process gave all the minerals in the lava time to crystallise; that is why these dikes, consisting of a kind of rock known as *granular*, which solidified rapidly in contact with the air, cannot continue the process of crystallisation that was begun in the depths below.

The rocks caused by the overflowing of lava generally consist of a small proportion of crystals and of a considerable vitreous mass, the chemical composition of which is that of the amorphous mixture of non-crystallised minerals. Unlike these rocks, a dike is an intrusive rock. Intrusive rock is never exposed to the atmosphere except as a result of erosion, which in the course of thousands of years wears away the vitreous rock or (what is more frequently the case) the sedimentary rock that covers them. And in the same way there are various other kinds of intrusive bodies, from the dike, an intrusive rock on a small scale, to those immense masses of granite known as batholiths; between these there are numerous others, all bearing outlandish names, since attempts have been made to define the shape and the volume by means of Greek roots.

(g) And what of the poets? All in all, they have made very little use of the source of imagery provided by the outbursts of the tellurian furnaces. Even Hugo's vast historical epic, 'La Légende des Siècles,' no more than pauses for an instant on the 'terrible threshold' of Momotombo.

> '*O ancient Momotombo, naked and bald colossus,*
> *Dreaming by the sea's edge, and of your crater making*
> *A shadowy and flaming crown for Earth . . .*'

There are some passages in Leconte de Lisle's and in Heredia's verse. And Baudelaire, in the *Fleurs du Mal*, makes figurative use of the upsurging of lava to indicate the explosion of fleshly desire in that haunted desert where

> '*Saint Anthony has seen, like lava heaving into sight,*
> *The crimson naked breasts of his temptations.*'

As for Dante, one would certainly expect his poem of the everlasting fire to have some volcanoes in it. Yet, even though the hollow cone of the Inferno, with its concentric circles going down deeper and deeper, does now and then somewhat suggest the vision of a sink-hole, there is no allusion in the text that would encourage us to think that the poet ever thought of such a resemblance. In his exile, on his travels, the Tuscan poet never visited the south of Italy; and it is perhaps a pity. And so we can only call it the inspiration of genius that enabled him, in his description of the 'snow-storm of fiery flakes', to call up before our eyes a picture of the inexorable showers of white-hot lapilli and to make us imagine the torture of the damned on burning ground that forces them to keep up a ghastly perpetual dance, just as though they were indeed on the scorching rim of a crater in eruption. Dante also describes the wall of fire—indeed a lava flow—that he has to cross in order to reach Beatrice, and how his flesh shrinks from it. Even Rimbaud did not go so far in finding flashes of glaring red for his *Saison en Enfer*. At the most a few flakes of lava splash here and there in the *Illuminations*. 'These fires in the diamond rain-storms thrown off by the mortal heart eternally turned into coal . . .'

The poem that will celebrate the volcano has yet to be written.

ACIDIC: Rock is described as acidic when it contained more than 60 per cent of silica (Si O,), either in the free state or in combination.

ANDESITE (from the Cordillera of the Andes, where these rocks were first studied by Leopold von Buch): Acidic lava, containing about 60 per cent silica, many soda-lime feldspars (from oligoclase to labradorite), and ferro magnesian minerals. It is porphyritic in structure, that is to say, it is made up of large crystals (of feldspar) floating in a micro-crystalline *paste*. The celebrated *red porphyry* (*porfido rosso*) of the ancients is an andesite. This lava is emitted by the majority of the volcanoes in the Pacific Belt of Fire (Krakatoa, Bandaisan, Tarawera, etc.) and by the great explosive volcanoes in general (Mount Pelée, Soufrière on Saint Vincent, and so on).

AUGITE: An important mineral in rock, belonging to the pyroxene group (ferro magnesian meta-silicates). Very common in the basalts.

BASALTS: Lavas belonging to the sub-division of the basic rocks. Dark in colour, turning brown, relatively rich in iron and magnesium. When the basalts are emitted in thick flows, convection currents arise in the interior of the layer that is in process of cooling down, and polygonal cells are formed; through solidification, these cells petrify, producing the columnar structure that is so famous (basaltic organs): the Giant's Causeway in Northern Ireland, Bortes-les-Orgues in Auvergne, and so on.

BASIC: Rock is described as basic when its percentage of silica (Si O,), either in combination or in the free state, is less than 60 or indeed 55. This increases the proportion of ferro magnesian minerals, and the colour of the rock darkens accordingly.

BOMBS: Lava projectiles thrown out of a crater by the *explosive* action of the gases. They may be spherical, elliptical, or discoidal, solid or hollow. They may be any size, from that of a nut to that of a railway-waggon. Their shape is due to their rotation in the air in the course of their trajectory, while they are still pasty.

CALDERA or CAULDRON: *See* Appendix I (*d*).

CRATER: A depression, generally funnel-shaped, sometimes bowl-shaped, forming the outlet of a volcanic vent. From the Greek κρατήρ, a bowl.

FELDSPAR: A very important group of minerals found in rock, consisting of aluminium silicate with potassium (K), sodium (Na), calcium (Ca), and barium (Ba). They may be colourless (rare), white, pink, yellow or green. The chief feldspars are orthoclase, microcline, albite, oligoclase, andesine, bytownite, and labradorite.

LAPILLI: *See* Appendix I (*a*).

MAGMA: A molten substance, an extremely viscous pseudo-solid fluid, found under the crust of the earth. Its composition is that of the basic rocks such as the basalts, gabbros, etc. The temperature is in the region of and even exceeds 2,000 degrees centigrade and the pressure ten or twenty thousand pounds per square inch.

OBSIDIAN: Volcanic glass. Acidic black lava (rich in silica). *See* PUMICE.

OLIVINE: Mineral found in basic rocks, especially in the ultra-basic (i.e. those very poor in silica). (Ferro magnesian ortho-silicate).

PUMICE: Volcanic *glass*, so porous that it is like solidified froth. The dissolved gases that separate from the liquid mass at the moment of solidification make it swell into this frothy consistency. If the external pressure had been greater, it would have prevented the development of these gas-bubbles and the same magma would have produced obsidian. In fact, obsidian melted in the crucible does produce pumice.

QUARTZ: Crystallised silica. This is the mineral most commonly found in nature. Pure sand is nothing but quartz. There are semi-precious varieties: agate, amethyst, cat's-eye, chalcedony, flint, jasper, onyx.

RHYOLITE: Igneous rocks of very acidic composition. Indeed, this kind of lava is the richest in silica. Chemically it corresponds to the granites, which are produced by the same magma, which has, however, consolidated slowly in the depths, so permitting crystals to form, whereas the rapid cooling of rhyolite ejected from a vent permits the formation only of fine-grained crystals immersed in an amorphous paste.

SIAL: The name given to the rocks that form the greater part of the continents and of the earth's crust (see SIMA) to a depth of 12 to 50 miles. It is so called from silica (Si) and aluminium (Al), the essential constituents of these rocks.

SIMA: The name given to the silico (Si)-magnesian (Ma for Mg) magma found below sial and gushing to the surface in the form of basalt. The floor of the Pacific is an exception, in having no crust of sial; it consists of solid crystalline sima. The explanation presumably lies in what appears to be the origin of that ocean: it would seem to be the scar left on the surface of the earth by the tearing off of the moon. At the time when the solidification of the globe had only just begun, our satellite seems to have been torn out of earth (for reasons both physical and mechanical), wrenching away with it the thin shell of solid sial and a certain amount of the basaltic coat immediately underneath.

SINK-HOLE: *See* Appendix I (*d*).
SPATTER-CONE: See p. 86.

The names in brackets are those of volcanoes that have not shown any signs of activity during the historical era.

In heavy black type: the volcanoes whose eruptions are very frequent or very violent.

The order of the names for each region corresponds roughly with a movement from north to south and from west to east.

The altitude of the chief volcanoes is given, likewise certain dates (of violent eruptions or the last observed period of activity).

A.—ATLANTIC

Jan Mayen
   Beerenberg

Iceland
   Leirhafnarskord
   Krafla
   Leirhnukur
   Dalfjall
   Hrossadalur
   Sveinagja
   Bjarnarflag
   Askja 1875
   Kverkfjoll
   (Kolottadyngza)
   (Herdubreid)
   (Trolladyngja)
   Ogmundarhraun
   Meitill

Brenniateinsfjoll
Eldeyar
Selyogsheidi
Krakatindur 1913
Hekla (5,110 ft.) 1845, 1947
Eldgja
Eyafjalla
Katla (5,250 ft.) 1918
Laki (2,740 ft.) 1783, over 20 miles (10,000 dead)
Vatna Jökull
Grimsvotn
Oraefa Jökull (6,950 ft.) 1727, 1783

Azores

São Miguel (3,570 ft.) 1630, 1811
Terceira
São Jorge
Pico
Fayal

Canary Islands

Teneriffe (12,180 ft.)
Lanzarote
Paima (7,730 ft.) 1949

Cape Verde Islands

Fogo
6 important submarine eruptions on the Equator at 20° W.
Mount Cameroon (13,350 ft.)
(Ascension Island)

Lesser Antilles

38 active volcanoes from North to South
Mt. Misery (St. Christopher)
Soufrière (Guadeloupe)
Grande Soufrière (Dominica)
Mt. Pelée (Martinique) (4,435 ft.) 1851, 1902 (40,000 dead),
        1929
Qualibou (St. Lucia)
Soufrière (St. Vincent) (4,050 ft.) 1902, 1929

B.—Europe

Mt. Albano (Monte Cavo, 3,110 ft.)
Salfatara de Puzzuoli (3,930 ft.)
Monte Nuovo (460 ft.) 1538, 1539
Vesuvius (3,280 ft.) 79 A.D., 1906, 1929, 1943
Epomeo
Stromboli (3,040 ft.) 1930 (5 dead)
Vulcano (1,640 ft.) 1888–90
Etna (10,860 ft.) 1669 (100,000 dead), 1928, 1949, 1950
Pantelleria
Giulia
5 submarine eruptions
Methana
Kos A.D 900.
Nisyros 1888
Santorini 1925, 1926
Submarine eruptions in the Sea of Azov 1950

C.—Africa

Eritrea
  Dubbi (4,198 ft.) 1861
  Afdera (7,297 ft.) 1907

Kenya, Tanganyika
  Teleki (1,902 ft.) 1896, 1919
  Sugobo
  (Menengai)
  (Longonot)
  (Suswa)
  (Shombole)
  (Gelei)
  Oldonyo l'Engai (9,374 ft.) 1945
  (Elanairobi)
  (Oloimoti)
  (Ngorongoro)
  (Kerimassi)
  (Lemagrut)
  (Oldeani l'Engai)

(Loomalassin)
(Kitumbeine)
(Meru) (14,960 ft.)
(Kilimanjaro) (19,610 ft.)
(Rungwe)

Central Africa
Nyamlagira (9,840 ft.) 1938, 1940, 1948 (Kituro)
Niragongo (11,500 ft.)
(Sabinyo)
(Muhavura) (13,120 ft.)
(Karisimbi) (14,760 ft.)

D.—INDIAN OCEAN

Submarine eruptions
Pondichéry 1757
Aden

Comoro Islands
Kartala (8,037 ft.) 1904

Reunion Is.
Piton De La Fournaise (8,248 ft.) 1900 to 1910, 1913, 1915, 1917, 1920, 1924, etc.

Kerguelen Islands
Heard Island 1910

E.—ASIA

Asia Minor
Ardschich Dagh (12,990 ft.)

Arabia
Harraten Nar
Schada
El Bedr

Armenia, Iran
  (Ararat)
  (Demavend)

Manchuria
  Ujun Choldongi
  Tuschan

F.—Indonesia

Sumatra
  Solawaik Agam
  Burni Telong
  Goenoeng
  Penet Sague
  Sorieg Berapi
  Tandikat
  Marapi
  Indrapura
  Talang
  Kaboe
  Dempo
  Krakatoa (2,620 ft.) 1883 (36,000 dead)

Java
  Danoe
  Karang
  Poelsari
  Satak
  Gede
  Tangkoeban Prahoe (6,800 ft.)
  Goentoer
  Papandayan (8,725 ft.) 1772 (3,000 dead), 1926
  Galung Gung (7,348 ft.) 1822 (4,000 dead), 1930
  Tjareme (10,100 ft.)
  Slamat
  Dieng
  Sendoro
  Merbabu
  Merapi (9,430 ft.) 1931 (1,300 dead)

Lawoe
Adikawilis
Keluit (5,680 ft.) 1586 (10,000 dead), 1919 (5,600 dead)
Tengger Bromo (7,862 ft.)
Semeru (12,055 ft.)
Lamongan
Ringgit (4,100 ft.)
Idjen
Raung (10,920 ft.)
More than 42 others dormant for over 500 years, at least.

Sumbawa Island

Tamboro (9,185 ft.) 1815 (12,000 dead, 29 survivors)

Moluccas

Awoe
Banua Wuhu
Siao
Roewang
Tonkoko
Empung
Lokon
Rumengen
Sempu
Sopoetan
Oena Oena
Tala
Ibu
Gamma Kunowa
Ternate
Motir
Makjan
Api Banda
Serua
Nila
Tijante

Bali

Bator

Agoeng
Api Sangean

Flores
Ija
Egon
Leworoh
Lobetobi
Jlimandiri
Komba
Boleng
Daan

G.—PACIFIC OCEAN

Kamchatka
Shevelyuch (10,500 ft.) 1854
Klyuchev (16,130 ft.)
Great Tolbatchik
Little Tolbatchik
Kountchokla
Kisimen
Ouson
Kihpinitch
Great Semiatchik
Little Semiatchik
Choupanov
Koryakshaya
Avacha
Moutnovskaya Sopka
Assatcha
Ksoudatch (3,510 ft.) 1907

Kuril Islands
Alaïd
Mosakiriyama
Firepeak
Kuroishima
Harimkotanshima
Chirin

Kotanshima
Ekaramashima
North Peak
South Peak
Ralkokeshima
Matuashima
Ketoishima
Shinsheridake
Chirnoishima
Suribachiyama
Moyorodake
Chiriporupuri

Japan
Raushidake
Rausuyama
Optateshike
Tokachi
Meakandake
Tarumaidaku
Usudake
Komogatake
Esan
Kama Fuseyama
Iwakiyama
Ugol
Kampuzan
Iwatesan
Komakadake
Chokaizan
Zaosan
Asamayama
Adatarasan
Bandai-San (6,440 ft.) 1888 (460 dead)
Nasuyama
Nikko
Tateyama
Kusatsu
Iwodake
Asamayama
Hakusan

Fujisan
Hakome
Oshima
Makakejima
Ikenosawo
Aogashima
Aso
Kirishima
Sakurashima 1914
Haimondake

Ryukyu Islands
Iwoshima
Shindake
Nakanoshima
Suwanoseshima
Ryukyu

Bonin Island
Minami Iwojima

Marianas Islands
Urakas Assongsong

South of Formosa
Submarine volcanoes

Philippines
Babuyan Claro
Didica
Camiguin
Cagua
Taal (1,050 ft.) 1911
Maquilin
Banajao
Mayon (9,030 ft.) 1914
Bulusan
Biliran
Kasiboi
Danan

Malaspina
Kamiguin Del Sur
Calayo
Magasu
Macaturin
Solo
Apo

New Guinea, New Pomerania
Garnot 1616
Blosseville 1700
Lesson
Manan
Krakar
Ritter 1888
Below Berg
Hunstein
Pango 1911, 1912
Loloban
Vater
Sudsohn
Ghaie 1878
Raluan 1878

Solomon Islands
Bagana
Savo
Sawaii

Samoa
Manua

Tonga (Friendly) Islands
Niuafou (590 ft.) 1886, 1919, 1947
Amargura 1846, 1847
Late 1854
Metis 1858
Tofua
Falcon Island
Frequent submarine eruptions

New Hebrides
  Tinakoro
  Ambrim
  Tana
  Fearn

Kermadec Islands
  Raoul 1870, 1872
  Magauley I 1825

Hawaii
  Mauna Loa 1950
  Kilauea 1924
  (Haleakala)
  (Mauna Kea)

New Zealand
  White Island 1914
  Tarawera 1886
  Tongariro
  Ngauruhoe (7,650 ft.)
  Ruapehu

Antarctic
  Erebus (13,330 ft.)

H.—North America

Aleutians
  Little Sitkin
  Sitignak
  Semisopochnoi
  Gareloi
  Tanaga
  Kanaga
  Adak
  Great Sitkin
  Koniushi
  Serguejeyski
  Volcan Conique

Korovin
Kliutchevskoy
Sarytchev
Siguam
Amarchta 1786
Yunaska
Tanach Angunach
Kigamiljach
Tchegulach
Retchechnoi
Vsevidov
Tulik
Bogoslov (Island)
Makouchine
Akun
Pogrumnoi
Shishaldin
Khaginak
Sannak

Alaska

Redoubt
Iliamna
St. Augustine
Kugak
Knife Volcano
Katmai (7,500 ft.) 1912
Novarupta
Mageik
Mt. Martin
Veniaminoff
Pavlov
Medwenikowski
Morshoyski
Shishaldin
Caroli
Mt. Wrangell (14,000 ft.)
Mt. Blackburn (16,140 ft.)
Mt. Sanford (15,870 ft.)
Mt. Edgecombe
Mt. Calder

U.S.A.

Mt. Baker (10,800 ft.) 1859, 1860
Mt. Rainier (15,440 ft.) 1843
Mt. St. Helens (11,770 ft.) 1907
Mt. Hood (11,770 ft.) 1907
Lassen Peak(10,440 ft.) 1916, 1926
The Three Virgins (6,540 ft.) 1857
Mt. Shasta (13,780 ft.)

I.—CENTRAL AMERICA

Between 18° and 22° N. 4° E. and 6° W. of Mexico

Cerro de S. Juan
Ceboruco 1870, 1875
Colima (12,000 ft.) 1913
Jorullo (4,330 ft.) 1759
Ajusco
Popocatepetl (17,945 ft.)
Orizaba (18,300 ft.) 1687
Tuxtla (5,080 ft.)
Parícutin (1,310 ft.) 1943 to 1950

Between 13° and 15° Lat. N. and 87°30′ and 92° Long. W.

Tacana 1855
Tajumulco
Cerro Auemado 1785
(San Antonio)
(Lacandon)
(Chicaval)
Santa Maria (12,360 ft.) 1902 (6,000 dead)
(Santo Tomas)
Azufral
Zunil
(S. Pedro)
(S. Clara)
Toliman
Atitlan
Acatenango
Fuego (12,580 ft.) 1717, 1799, 1932

(Pacaya)
(Jumay)
(Cerro Redondo)
(Cerro Alto)
(Sumasate)
(Tecuamburro)
(Ipala)
(Monte Rico)
(Tahual)
(Iztepeque)
(Cerro Colorado)
(S. Catarina)
(Buenavista)
(Culma)
Izalco (6,200 ft.) 1770, 1926
S. Ana
S. Marcelino
S. Salvador 1917
Playon
Boqueroncitos
Boqueron
Ilopango 1880
S. Vicente
Tecapa
Chinameca
S. Miguel (7,000 ft.) 1825
Conchagua
Conchaguita 1892
Coseguina (3,800 ft.) 1835

Between 10° *and* 13° *Lat. N. and* 83° 30' *and* 87° *Long. W.*

El Viego
Chichigalpa
Telica
Las Pilas 1914, 1923
Momotombo (4,125 ft.) 1905
Masaya
Ometepe
Gongora 1849
Rincon de la Vieja 1922
Miravalles

Tenorio
Poas (8,780 ft.) 1927
Barba
Turrialba
Irazu (11,325 ft.) 1723, 1917

J.—South America

Between 5° Lat. N., 2° Lat. S. and 75° Long. W. and 80° Long W.

Mesa Nevada de Herveo
Ruiz
Tolima (18,125 ft.)
Huila
Purace (15,420 ft.) 1949
(Sotara)
(Pan de Azucar)
(Petacas)
(Animas)
Dona Juana (13,940 ft.) 1899
Tajumbina
Galeras (13,975 ft.)
Pasto (13,990 ft.'
(Bordoncillo)
Tuquerres
Cumbal
(Chiles)
(Imbabura)
(Cayambe)
Pichincha (15,700 ft.)
(Atacatzo)
(Corazan)
(Jlinitza)
Antisana (18,880 ft.)
(Sincholagua)
Cotopaxi (19,590 ft.) 1877 (1,000 dead) 1903
(Quillinoana)
Guacamayo
(Carihuairazo)
(Chimborazo)
Tungurahua (16,890 ft.)

(Altar)
Sangai (18,770 ft.)

Cordillera Range, Andes

Active volcanoes counted from N. to S.:
Licancaur (19,450 ft.)
S. Pedro (18,700 ft.)
Lascar (19,260 ft.)
Isluga (18,140 ft.)
Llullaillaco (21,720 ft.)
Aconcagua (22,970 ft.)
Antofalla
Copiapo
Tupungato
San Jose (16,400 ft.)
Maipo (17,390 ft.)
Tinguirica (14,435 ft.) 1932
Peteroa (13,320 ft.)
Descabezado (3,940 ft.) 1932
Cerro Azul
Chillan (9,450 ft.)
Antuco (8,857 ft.)
Punmahuida
Lonquimay (9,480 ft.)
Llaima (10,100 ft.)
Villarica (9,510 ft.)
El Mocho
Renihue (1,000 ft.)
Osorno (7,380 ft.)
Calbuco (5,700 ft.)
Huequi
Minchinmavida (8,100 ft.)
Corcovada (7,640 ft.)
Yanteles (6,725 ft.)
Mt. Burnley 1910
Las Yeguas 1932
Zuizapu 1932